Charlotte Buckhaven, daugh̲̅ ̲̅ ̲̅ ̲̅ ̲̅ ̲̅ ̲̅ ̲̅ ̲̅ ̲̅ ̲̅ ̲̅ was educated at Queen Anne's S̲̅ ̲̅ ̲̅ ̲̅ ̲̅ ̲̅ ̲̅ ̲̅ ̲̅ ̲̅ ̲̅rs- ity. She was a working barris̲̅ ̲̅ ̲̅ ̲̅ ̲̅ ̲̅ ̲̅ ̲̅ ̲̅ ̲̅ ̲̅to have a family. She now lives ̲̅ ̲̅ ̲̅ ̲̅ ̲̅ ̲̅ ̲̅ ̲̅ ̲̅ ̲̅ ̲̅eir two children. *Barrister By an̲̅ ̲̅ ̲̅ ̲̅ ̲̅ ̲̅*

Charlotte Buckhaven
Barrister By and Large

Pan Books London and Sydney

First published 1985 by Michael Joseph Ltd
This edition published 1986 by Pan Books Ltd
Cavaye Place, London SW10 9PG
9 8 7 6 5 4 3 2 1
© Charlotte Buckhaven 1985
ISBN 0 330 29225 0
Printed and bound in Great Britain by
Richard Clay (The Chaucer Press) Ltd,
Bungay, Suffolk

For my mother,
with love

1

I was delighted with myself. It had been an outstanding performance. My speech had been smooth yet firm, nicely paced, well
delivered. A barristerial smirk began sneaking across my face. At
this moment I could have swept the whole court away on the
wind of my eloquence. It was a pity I had had only two sentences
to say.

'And therefore . . .' I snapped my brief together in a professional
manner, 'I would ask your lordship to make the usual order.'

From his throne somewhere near the rafters the judge looked
down, adjusting the half-moon glasses on his thin nose as though
to focus on something he had noticed creeping up a wastepipe.
'Ah yes, the *usual* order, Miss er . . .' he whispered in a little voice
as dry as papyrus. 'And what order, exactly, do you mean by that?'

What order? Feverishly I dredged my memory for an answer but
it was hopeless. I had no idea. 'Get up and give him the facts as
briefly as you can,' a senior member of my chambers had advised.
'Old Razor Bill's a cranky bastard; no need to annoy him by going
into details. Ask him to make the usual order; he'll know what
you mean.'

'Well, Miss er. . . ?'

If he did know what I meant, the judge was showing no sign of
it. I must think of something to say. I could not stand here dumb,
like a public buffoon, with the eyes of my instructing solicitor
boring into my back. His embarrassment on my behalf was like a
living presence breathing down my neck. Perhaps I could pretend
to faint? No: that would make matters worse. I should feel more
conspicuous than ever being lugged out of court by the usher. I
could no longer think. My concentration had become fixed on a
knothole in the wooden desk in front of me. Glossy-brown and
ringed like a contour map, it seemed to be doing a queer country
dance in time to a muffled drum thumping in my head.

Seconds ticked by. I cursed myself. How could I have over-looked something so vital? I was a complete fool, not fit to call myself a barrister. The knothole advanced and retreated. The drumbeat was the only sound in a stifling silence. Pull yourself together, I snapped at myself. Everyone makes mistakes. Think of it as a lesson for the future . . . But what future? Would there be one? Desperately I scratched my head through a hole in my wig and hoped the court building might fall down.

At moments like this scenes from past life are supposed to flash before one's eyes. I was aware of an increasing sense of unreality in which the court and everybody in it seemed to be receding away into haze . . .

What was I doing here? Why had I always wanted to be a barrister of all things? Why not something more suited to my powers of quick thinking: snail-farming in the Outer Hebrides, for example? Some quirk of fate or character must have led me along this road; or perhaps the thought of holding spellbound a courtroom full of people who were not allowed to get up and leave? One thing was certain: this moment, nasty though it was, was the result of years of ambition. I saw my slow progress again: from a stout child puffing to the top of the garden wall to declaim poetry to startled passers-by; to a student over the midnight oil, stuffing in a vast hotchpotch of parrot-learning about how slaves were freed in ancient Rome or bees caught, about contracts and carbolic smokeballs, trusts, decomposing molluscs in ginger-beer containers, torts, and the terrible Rule in *Foss* v. *Harbottle* which always held for me all the horrors of the unknown. Now I saw myself in the dark Old Hall at Lincoln's Inn fearfully turning over the crisply printed examination paper:

'*Foss* v. *Harbottle* was a watershed. Discuss.'

It had been a long road but one trodden in the hope that the putting on of a wig and gown would automatically turn me into a sort of latter-day Marshall Hall. And where had it brought me? To where I stood now, on the brink of being publicly pecked to death by that dreadful old vulture up there. It was like being a ninepin, I thought – up one moment, bowled over the next. If I had only known . . .

But wait, had I not been given a warning on the very evening of my call to the bar? Surely I should have learned then that, whenever Fortune seems to shake you by the hand, public ridicule is generally creeping up behind with the banana skin.

Suddenly I was back at the Middle Temple, re-living my call-night nine months before. It was a June evening. Since morning London had simmered in blazing sunshine. By late afternoon the day was still hot and the Union Jack on the Temple flagstaff hung motionless against a clear blue sky. A shaft of evening sunlight filtered through the leaves of the old mulberry tree, dappling the flagstones of the quadrangle with liquid gold and casting lengthening shadows across the smoothly shaved lawns which rolled down to the river.

Outside the Middle Temple Hall a small crowd had begun to gather, garden-party silks and dark suiting mingling as visitors strolled along the walk beside the goldfish pool. From the open windows of chambers around the square a distant tapping of typewriters punctuated the gentle hum of conversation which rose above the splash and ripple of the fountain and the occasional rustling of leaves in soft summer breeze. From this quiet oasis in the hurly-burly city the boom of homegoing traffic outside the Temple gates seemed no more than a far-off intimation of an age to come.

As I passed, I saw the first young man lope down the Hall steps with a nonchalance which announced that he was on his maiden voyage in wig and gown. More followed him into the square, pushing into the gathering crowd to claim relatives; some in twos and threes, others surrounded by mothers, sisters and girlfriends. Commonwealth students posed beaming in the Hall porch for the cameras of family and friends and of the odd passing tourist who had paused to record the scene, puzzled as to what was going on but taken up in the general atmosphere of expectancy.

In the ladies' cloakroom of the Library I fought with a stiff wing-collar. Having made stud holes in it front and back, the makers had then cunningly disguised the holes by starching them together. Why, I could not guess. In fact I found it hard to guess who could possibly have designed such an article of clothing in the first place or for what purpose. To mortify the flesh perhaps, I thought, grimly grappling with a springy adversary which seemed in better physical condition than myself. It was a mean opponent. Every time I anchored one end under my chin the other at once sprang up and whacked me in the eye. Once the thing escaped altogether and shot off into a corner. I found it crouched beneath a radiator and we closed in combat again. This time I manoeuvred the back stud through the back hole and had the two front holes lined up correctly when the front stud added an unfair new dimension to the contest by suddenly folding up on itself so that I missed the collar altogether and stuck the stud firmly into my neck. By the end of fifteen minutes the collar looked as tired as I felt. Hastily I tied a pair of starched white bands around it in a loose damp bow and scraped my hair back into a sort of knob which I fancied looked professional. I pulled on my black jacket and eagerly drew from its cardboard box my brand new gown, shaking out the folds so that the heavy black stuff gleamed dully in the evening light.

Feeling bulky and important I turned to face the mirror. The reflection which peered back bore no resemblance to the masterful advocate I had hoped to see. What it had was the keen and crumpled look of a newly hatched beetle. The gown was still full of wrinkles. Had I been right in buying one three sizes too large? I had pictured the sweep of it behind me as I passed grandly along corridors, but now it looked like a dismantled tent, drooping to the floor all around me and making my skirt look ridiculously short. The bands sagged below the front collar-stud, one end of which was lodged in my windpipe. The wing-collar, uneasy in defeat, had now grown sabre teeth which poked upwards into my jawbone so that to see straight ahead I had to crane my neck up and peer down my nose like a camel. Half an hour ago it had been hard enough to believe that I was about to become a barrister; now it was impossible.

Hastily I smoothed as many wrinkles as possible from the gown and hoisted the bands. I put on my wig, a fine old war-bonnet which had ridden into battle on a succession of heads more distinguished than my own. Over the years all the thinking, or smoking, going on beneath had warmed the horsehair to a rich amber-grey, and the effect brought a touch of dignity to my raw ensemble. I was vain enough to be glad that it also hid most of the beetle hairdo. Although perhaps not a sight to inspire much professional confidence, I at least looked like a human being.

I was pausing to savour the moment, when the clock in the Strand began to strike six. Grabbing the marquee-like folds of my gown with one hand and holding on the wig with the other, I flapped out of the library block and ran up Middle Temple Lane.

As I came within sight of the square my fears were confirmed: barristers, visitors – everyone – had gone. Seized by panic, I made a rush towards the doors. At the foot of the porch steps I suddenly saw my parents waiting, hatted, silked and pinstriped for the occasion. My anxiety was momentarily forgotten. What a proud moment it would be for them when they saw me in my finery. My mother might burst into tears at the sight, I thought with satisfaction – my father too, perhaps. Yes, it was a moving moment for us all. If they were not struck wordless by emotion, what would they say to me? I stopped in front of them with an expectant smile.

'Oh, Charlotte . . .' my mother said. 'You're so *late*. The others went in ten minutes ago.'

'Pull your bands up, your stud's showing,' said my father.

Disgusted, I puffed on into the cool darkness of the porch and the great doors swung together behind me.

The panelled hallway within was also deserted. Although I could hear the distant rattle of crockery as the Inn staff prepared for dinner, there was no one to be seen. I jumped when one of the white-jacketed stewards, round and pink-nosed as a rabbit, suddenly popped out of a doorway to my left.

'That way, madam.' He pointed down the passage and, seeing him glance at his watch, I hurried past the Great Hall towards the inner recesses reserved for the Masters of the Bench who govern the Inn. Strange to think that when I sat down to dinner in Hall tonight it would no longer be in the short gown of a student but in all the grand paraphernalia of a barrister. The drab duckling about to change into a swan could hardly have been more full of delighted anticipation.

I could hear a babbling sound up ahead and another turn along the passageway brought me to a handsome oak-panelled smoking room where I at last ran the other candidates for call to earth, assembled over preliminary thimbleful of sherry. I was met at the threshold by a conversational hubbub and a blast of steamy heat. The smallish room was stuffed to bursting with four or five dozen people, most of them as thickly dressed as I; the atmosphere, although festive, was stifling. A friend sticking up through the crush a yard or so away saw me and waved cheerily.

'Hello, Charlotte. So you've come, have you?' he shouted in a welcoming tone. 'Jolly good. Didn't think I'd seen you. Decided you weren't here, as a matter of fact. Well, of course I was right.

You can't have been if you've just come, can you? I mean, could you?' He laughed heartily. 'By the way, it is you, isn't it?'

'Of course it's me.' I shouted above the racket, wondering how many thimblesful there had been before I arrived.

'I only ask because I was in the Devereux earlier. Saw a girl in a pink sundress. Thought, if that's Charlotte, it's a bit odd. See now it wasn't. Wasn't you, I mean – or odd, now I come to think of it. Do you think there's any more sherry coming round?'

'I shouldn't think so.' I shouted, looking at my watch. 'Have you got a mess arranged for dinner tonight?' Diners in the Inn sat on benches at great oaken refectory tables grouped into messes of four.

'I don't really know as such,' he howled back. 'There's about six of us dining but I don't know who's supposed to be in a group with who. Come along anyway. We can sort it out as we go along.'

'My father's sending a bottle of champagne down to my mess.'

'Ha. Tell you what. Let's you and I stick together whatever happens. . .'

Just then up came the students' officer, who was circulating the assembly doing her best to see that everybody looked presentable. She herself looked both elegant and cool and I wondered how she managed it until I remembered that in her silk dress she must be wearing ten pounds less of clothing than anyone else in the room.

'Yes, that's fine, Miss Hunter,' she said kindly. 'But I'm afraid your bands are coming down, and do you think you could have rather less hair showing under your wig?'

Remembering the beetle hairdo, I was surprised, but on investigation found that all the running I had done had unfastened the knob. I must look like Little Orphan Annie. Hastily I started searching through my pockets for hairgrips.

'Now, gentlemen, gentlemen, please, may I have your attention? I'm sorry but Master Treasurer has said that the last time wigs were allowed to be removed for call ceremony was, he believes, in June 1949, which was apparently a rather hotter evening than this – so, although it is rather warm tonight, I'm afraid you'll have to do your best to put up with it.'

This announcement produced an epidemic of wig-lifting and brow-mopping all over the room and I was thankful that my own wig, which had for generations been too old to be mended, was full of holes which provided quite good ventilation. On the minus side was the fact that it had for the same length of time been too old to be cleaned, so that any rise in temperature would make it give off a strange smell which put me in mind of polecats. Even now I caught sight of one or two people gazing curiously in my direction.

'Now, gentlemen, I think we are ready to go into Hall, so if you would be good enough to get into line in the order in which I am about to call your names we shall be able to make a start. Mr Abu, over here please; Mr Akchuku, Mr Adams, Mr Badruddin . . .'

We stood in the Great Hall lined shoulder to shoulder in a battle formation four rows deep. As each name was called, the person standing at the nearside front would step forward. The whole row would then shuffle one pace to the left, giving the impression of a solemn ritual dance being performed by a troupe of penguins. The man on my right stood out from our black and white ranks like a bird of paradise in a splendid uniform covered with golden bobbles, buttons and braid and complete with a dress sabre which clanked whenever he shuffled.

. . . One two three, shuffle. One two three, clank.

High above us the black vault of a roof spanned by vast double hammerbeams four hundred years old soared skywards in dark majesty. Towering stone walls lined with oak panelling twenty feet high and surmounted by the armour of crusader knights, the first Templars, gleamed in a half-light which showed intricately depicted on every panel the crest of a Reader of the Inn. I watched as a last shaft of evening sun slanting down through the mullioned lights of ornamented windows overhead touched the eastern wall, bringing suddenly to life an emblazoned tapestry of armorial red, blue and gold.

. . . One two three, shuffle. One two three, clank.

On the dais before us stood two gowned Masters of the Bench: Master Treasurer and the Reader, who was presenting to him the candidates in order from a long list. As each stepped forward, the Treasurer pronounced the ceremonial words of call to the bar and shook the hand of the new barrister, who would then pass on to sign his name in a huge leatherbound book before returning to his place at the other end of the row.

. . . One two three, shuffle. One two three, clank.

The face of each student as he came forward to be called

showed the same blend of pride and secret disbelief. For those from overseas, smiling and immaculate in dazzling new white wigs, this day marked a triumph of persistence in the face of difficulty; the end of many months of grind in a cold and inhospitable capital. Here was the accolade at last: the right of each to record his name in that historic book in which so many famous names had been inscribed. Here too was . . .

. . . Had I heard my own name?

Suddenly from some helpful colleague behind there came a tremendous shove which shot me forward with such speed that I cannoned past the Reader and only managed to stop myself by grasping at the Master Treasurer's outstretched hand.

'Master Treasurer,' the Reader was repeating, 'I present Miss Charlotte Hunter.'

The introduction was unnecessary; the Treasurer and I were already nose to nose. He stepped back a pace.

'Miss Hunter, in the name of the Masters of the Bench, I call you to the degree of the Utter Bar.'

I could almost hear trumpets. In my imagination carpets vast as the Red Sea uncoiled before me as I shook the Treasurer's hand and passed on in a blaze of glory. This was the pinnacle: a time for sackbuts and the crash of cymbals; my great moment whose memory would remain forever as vibrant and splendid as now . . .

My gown was tugged hard from behind. I was dragged sharply backwards billowing out like a parachute. I looked round in panic.

'The book,' someone hissed. 'Sign the book.'

Of course, the book. I had watched twenty-eight people perform the simple ceremony successfully and still managed to bungle it. Hot and embarrassed, I was scrawling my name as fast as I could on history's page when I realized that a queue was building up behind me. I dropped the pen and started to scuttle back to the end of the row. All might still have been well if I had not tripped over the dress sabre.

There were just the two of us in a mess that night at dinner and between us we polished off the champagne in true festival style followed by a bottle of wine. After that there was a grand family celebration with a second dinner and many toasts. I do not accept for a moment that I hiccuped for two hours and had to be carried to bed in my clothes – even though, to be truthful, my recollection of that part of the evening is a little woolly. Mercilessly clear in every detail however is the remembrance of the ghastly moments I spent flat on my face in all my regalia on the historic floor of the Middle Temple Hall. Also clear was the lesson to be learned from the experience and I ought to have remembered it: beware the banana skin; the law is full of surprises . . .

'Miss er, for the last time, are we to hear the nature of your application?'

Recollection faded. I was back on my feet in the companies' court with Old Razor Bill getting ready to come in for the kill. I swallowed hard. It was useless trying to put off the nasty moment any longer. Roars of derision sounded in my head, sardonic murmurings, twitters of mirth. Nasty was hardly the word; I would be crucified.

Just as I had finally given the situation up for lost I noticed a folded slip of white paper being passed from hand to hand along the barristers' row. My neighbour put it on the desk in front of me and I saw with a kind of dim surprise that it had my name on it. I had to read it twice before I understood, but as I did so my vision slowly cleared; my heart began to beat again and the terrible thumping in my head died away. I looked up at my tormentor on his throne.

'What I seek, my lord,' I said, 'is an order for the compulsory winding-up of this company under the provisions of Sections 222-225 of the Companies' Act 1948 together with an order for costs in favour of the petitioning creditor.'

Saved? I could hardly believe it. I still had a future – no snail-farm for me, after all. Looking back along the row, I fancied that I saw one of the senior bewigged figures give what was subtly but unmistakably a wink. One day I'll write a book, I thought . . . about the Bar and how it feels to be a newcomer to this peculiar life which can be so terrifying one moment, so hilarious the next; a life full of good fellowship, pomp and banana skins, whose only consistent feature is its capacity to surprise.

For I had just discovered that the colleague who had saved me from public shame was my opponent in the case.

Yes, I thought, as I slowly gathered up my papers to go; one day I'll write a book . . .

2

We were all being slowly steamed alive. Hot, damp and pallid as suet puddings, we rocked about sticking to each other. Squeezed intimately against a paunchy and unshaven man whose breakfast must have included a knob of garlic, I wondered if there could be a more drab start to a day than a journey in the London tube. On my very first morning as a pupil, I was going to be suffocated before I even reached chambers, I thought, straining away as a fresh acetylene blast hit me full in the face. Noisily the train hurled itself into a tunnel, then lost courage, shuddered to a halt and stood trembling in the darkness. The straphangers crashed into the seated passengers' newspapers and trampled on their feet. The rest of us subsided over each other like a falling cardhouse. As we were getting up again, the train suddenly pulled itself together and rushed into the station, where it stopped violently, causing fresh confusion. The doors rolled open and I pulled myself, my briefcase and my cloth wig-bag clear and plopped like a mailsack onto the platform. With a sigh, the train resealed itself and wound away into the tunnel, leaving behind a brief hot wind and the smell of sulphur.

It was airier on the platform but no cooler. This surprised me until I realized that the heat was inside my suit. I had been lucky enough to find this suit at half-price in a sale and I was very pleased with it. Not only had it been marvellous value but it seemed to have the professional touch. On my first day it was a comfort to know that I was looking my best. True, I was a little warm, but to have bought a summer suit as well would have been a silly extravagance. Yes, I thought, they certainly know how to build solid quality into clothes in Bulgaria. It was made of a thick, black, bobbly material, durable rather than soft, and there was a lot of it. Although these were the days of the mini, the skirt came well below my knees and the jacket, double-breasted with steel buttons and heavily padded shoulders, was almost as long. From the inside, it felt as though it had been welded rather than sewn together but I had hopes that it would become more flexible with wear.

As I moved up the steps my new shoes creaked. Or perhaps it was my feet – they felt terrible. The June sun beat hot on my blanketed back as I started along the Embankment towards the Temple. Everything was green: soft shades of haze over the river; brocaded lawns edged by the dark sweep of trees. This is a true milestone, the first day of my legal career, I thought, swinging my new blue wig-bag across my shoulder with a touch too much swashbuckle, so that the metal wig-box inside caught me rather painfully in the small of the back.

It seemed no more than moments before I caught my first glimpse of the tall brick building in which my pupilmaster had his chambers. I stopped and gazed up at it through the sunlit trees. It was unadorned, smooth and somehow forbidding. Even the sunshine playing in rose tones over the brick failed to soften the stern aristocracy of that Georgian façade. As I watched, one of the top-floor windows rattled upwards, breaking the stillness. Inside, the business day was beginning. Soon the grave, important-looking men whose preserve this was would start arriving: collecting piles of leather books, poring over documents, or doing whatever they did to prepare for the forensic cut and thrust. I was aware that I had a certain amount still to learn about the practical side of a barrister's work . . .

Although I knew something about the law, my knowledge of the workings of the profession into which I had so recently tumbled was almost nil. The examination course in those days was largely theoretical – so much a matter of memory, in fact, that I used to wonder if a reasonably bright African parrot would not have stood as good a chance as myself of qualifying as a barrister. I was curious to know what barristers did when they were not in court or drinking tea in the Middle Temple barristers' common room. Much of their work, I knew, consisted of reading papers sent by solicitors, the GPs of the legal profession, who wanted to be advised on some aspect of a case. Barristers, the legal specialists, looked up the law and wrote opinions; they settled pleadings, the statements of claim, defences, divorce petitions and the similar formal documents which have to be filed setting out the nature of a party's case at each stage of an action. What else they did I could only speculate. I had been inside a set of chambers no more than half a dozen times, and the only pleading I could have drafted was a statement of claim I had memorized from a textbook, about a storekeeper who had dropped through a trapdoor and broken a leg. I had never written an opinion in my life. The proper way of presenting a case in court was also a closed book to me. As a barrister, I would have been – except to some hypothetical injured storekeeper – absolutely useless. It is to protect the public from people like myself that the pupillage system was invented.

The twelve-month apprenticeship each barrister spends as the pupil of a senior practitioner is compulsory. By watching their masters in court, assisting them in any way they can, looking up the law for them, devilling their papers and generally getting underfoot, pupils begin to acquire a groundwork of practical knowledge – in the hope that, by the time they are allowed to take their first cases after six months, they will be, if not necessarily a great help to every client, at least not a positive hazard.

I started across the road. What would they make of me, those austere pinstriped beings up there? Would my being a girl make much difference or would they not notice? What would my pupilmaster be like? Visions of a fierce figure in robes came to mind and were not reassuring. I knew hardly any barristers. To us students, they were beings to be viewed from afar, scarcely to mingle with. A qualified person was as different from a student as a giant hawkmoth is from a caterpillar, and there was no middle stage between the two forms of life.

I had seen this sudden change in contemporaries who had been called to the Bar. They rounded out and became sleek. Paunches once hidden beneath baggy student sweaters now burgeoned grandly forth under the straining cloth of new waistcoats. Shaggy hair was slicked back to reveal shiny new hairlines. The speech became measured; the gait pompous. It was as though a floppy stuffed dog had been transformed into a painted wooden toy alderman. Since my own call to the bar, I had looked for some sign of increased stature in myself, but could find none. Apart from the new suit, I felt exactly the same.

I had just reached the high wrought-iron Temple gates when a girl and a boy ran past, both looking cool in jeans and T-shirts and each incongruously carrying a briefcase. Law students. You would have thought they could take the trouble to dress properly for lectures, I thought with a touch of irritation. Things had obviously changed since my time, and not for the better. I walked on through the gates and towards the pink building.

In a little square before the entrance I was greeted by what resembled a motor show. Much impressed, I looked over a display of gleaming boots and bonnets which seemed to include the entire range of famous names, from a vast silver Rolls in the far corner to an Italian sports model so exotic that it might have come from outer space. It was clear that I had chosen the right career. It was only many months later, as I sat in my tiny room overlooking the Temple bicycle shed, wondering how long it might take me to save up for a moped, that it struck me what a magnificently out-of-the-ordinary experience my pupillage had been.

Passing through a pair of swing-doors into the pink building, I found myself in a narrow stone hallway from which a flight of worn steps led upwards. It was cool and smelled pleasantly of caves. With a quick look round to be sure I was unobserved, I undid my jacket and fanned myself to let air in and steam out. Beneath my white nylon blouse I was now cold and clammy, but even that was an improvement. I fanned my face as well, hoping it looked less red than it felt. As my eyes adjusted to the gloom, I saw to the right a doorway leading to chambers on the ground floor. The heavy wooden outer door, which stood open, was painted black and listed on it in white were the names of the barristers working there. On the flat part at the top were two Queen's Counsel, then the list flowed down over the panelling to some extremely junior person whose name had been painted over beading and a keyhole and was so distorted as to be barely readable. The thought of how I would feel reading my own name on just such a door somewhere in the Temple one day excited me and bolstered my courage. Why should I not do as well as these other people? I had, after all, passed the examinations, which must show that I was either knowledgeable or lucky enough to make a success of this. I would beat the lot of them. I buttoned up my Bulgarian jacket firmly and picked up my baggage.

To my left in a corner was a lift which might at a pinch have accommodated two dwarfs. Someone had hung a cardboard notice on the door which read: LIFT UNSAFE. USE ONLY IN EMERGENCIES.

It was a stiffish climb up four stone flights and I had to stop on the landing outside the top floor to re-ventilate my jacket. While doing this, I read the door and saw that Mr Tobin's name was there, high up on the panelling. I looked at my watch. It was just after half past nine. I buttoned my jacket slowly, pulled the sleeves up and the white lacy cuffs of my blouse down. I cleared my throat. Then, because there seemed to be nothing else left to do, I turned the brass handle of the inner door.

It opened with a sigh, revealing a broad passageway furnished in Harley Street style with red Turkey carpeting and Chippendale dining chairs. One cream wall was lined with bookshelves and the other hung with Spy cartoons of antique lawyers, together, appropriately, with a large print of two old-time pugilists in longjohns squaring up to each other across a lush spider-plant on a mahogany stand. There was a pleasant smell of polish, leather and instant coffee. I could see nobody about. Skirting a low table on which two copies of the *Illustrated London News* had been carefully arranged, I headed down the passageway towards the sound of work coming from a doorway at the other end. The carpet felt thick and soft beneath my creaking feet. I passed several closed doors wondering which was my pupilmaster's and whether he had arrived. By now I was sweating in earnest and it had nothing to do with my suit. I tapped on the door which stood ajar, then after a time, as the noise inside went on unabated, poked my head into the room.

At first sight I thought I had strayed into a secondhand furniture shop in which some sort of paperchase had been going on. Into a small space had been crammed three or four desks and several tables, all littered with small items of office equipment. There seemed to be telephones all over the place, piles of ledgers and tottering wire baskets full of papers. On every spare surface including the floor were bundles of papers done up in pink tape, some thick with dust. A long-haired girl was pounding at a great old-fashioned typewriter by the window and behind the door a lad with the look of a bookmaker's clerk – a mug of coffee beside him and his feet up on the desk – was checking a long, closely printed list on which he paused to make entries from time to time with a stub of a pencil. At a huge desk facing the entrance sat a tired-looking greyish man in shirtsleeves talking alternately on two telephones.

Although I had hardly expected my appearance to cause a sensation, I was mildly surprised when, having glanced up to see who had come in, all three occupants carried on with what they were doing without a pause. I took up a position in front of the greyish man's desk and waited for him to finish on the telephones. After a time he hung up both, whereupon a third underneath a pile of stationery started buzzing like a hornet.

'Get it, Paul,' said the man, looking up. 'Yes, miss, what can we do for you?'

'Excuse me,' I said. 'My name's, er, Hunter.' I suddenly felt that to say 'Charlotte Hunter' would sound too feminine and silly. 'I'm Mr Tobin's new pupil. I hope I've come on the right day?'

The man smiled. He had a pleasant, friendly face when the exhaustion lifted from it.

'Ah yes, Miss Hunter, you're expected,' he said, to my relief – for I had begun to wonder. 'I don't know if Mr Tobin's in yet,' he went on, with a glance at a station clock hanging above the door. 'He generally gets in at 9.40 on the dot, or thereabouts. A great stickler for punctuality, Mr Tobin is. Very keen on his pupils getting in early.'

'I'm so sorry, I didn't realize,' I said.

'Never mind. It's only your first morning, after all. Now, I've just about time to give you a quick run-through about how things are done here.'

'Thank you very much.'

'Not at all. Now, Mr Tobin likes his pupils to come into the clerks' room here first thing each morning and check the diary – that's this.' He indicated a big leatherbound book on the desk before him. 'To see what he's got on.'

'I see. Thanks very much.'

'Not at all. Then when you've made a list of the cases – you can see for example here, today being Tuesday, he usually has quite a few in the undefended list over the road, six today.' He pointed to a number of pencilled entries in the book which appeared to be written in hieroglyphs. 'You'll find the briefs in his room. All right?'

'Right. Thanks very much,' I said, wondering what the undefended list was and where across the road it was to be found, but not liking to ask.

'Not at all. Now, Mr Tobin likes the briefs to be laid out on his desk for when he comes in, and in the proper order so that he can get into them straightaway without any distractions.' He looked at me quite severely, as though assessing whether I would provide any distractions, then seemed to decide that I would not. 'Great powers of concentration, Mr Tobin has, as you'll find,' he added.

'Yes, I'm sure,' I murmured heartily. It occurred to me that if Mr Tobin were able to prepare six briefs between 9.40 and half past ten his powers of concentration must be formidable.

'Now, get any papers he's been working on overnight and bring them in here for typing and put the others back in their proper place. It'll be your job to keep his papers in order. A stickler for tidiness, Mr Tobin is. Yes, a great stickler, as you'll discover.'

'I see.'

'Yes, and he'll also want you to be ready to look up any points of law in a hurry: go to the library if necessary, and give him a quick answer. All right?'

'Yes, thank you,' I said, somewhat daunted by this last item. Quick answers of any kind have never been a speciality of mine and I hoped Mr Tobin would not ask for many.

'Not at all. Now, when he leaves for court it'll be up to you to carry over any books he may require, and his robes and papers and so on. That is, of course, unless there's any need to impress the client – in which case, Paul here' – he indicated the lad, now rolling himself a cigarette – 'will be sent over to do the necessary.'

'Ah,' I said. I had a sudden lunatic vision of myself plodding across the road like a native carrier bent under piles of books, the six briefs, Mr Tobin's briefcase, my own, and our two wig-bags – while my pupilmaster strode ahead, tall, saturnine and silent in the manner of an old-time explorer: raking the horizon with hooded eyes in quest of the undefended list, engrossed in thoughts of a heavy day ahead, adversaries to be demolished, judges outmanoeuvred, cases won. (I found it hard to imagine that Mr Tobin with his powers of concentration would lose many cases.)

'Now, I've made out the list of cases for you here, so all you'll have to do is to look them out and put them ready for Mr Tobin.'

'I'm much obliged to you,' I said by way of a change.

'Not at all. Mr Tobin's room is that one there.' He pointed to one of the doors. 'Hope you'll enjoy being with us, Miss Hunter.'

'Thank you very much,' I said.

'Not at all,' said the grey man politely, moving a pile of wire baskets aside to locate a fourth telephone which had started shrilling somewhere on his desk.

Out in the passageway I looked at the list. The names of the cases were clearly printed in red biro. This ought to present no great problem, I thought with relief. I was anxious to make as good an impression as I could on Mr Tobin the stickler for timekeeping and tidiness. Since my interview with the grey man I found that my vague apprehension had crystallized into honest, full-blooded dread. I had as soon meet Henry VIII I thought, knocking on the door.

'Come,' rang out a voice which I felt must strike terror into witnesses by its sheer depth and volume.

Mr Tobin was as I had imagined, only greyer and bigger. For a moment I had the mad impression that a great walrus was looking at me from the depths of a leather wing chair before the window, for it was all there: the brilliant dark eyes and drooping moustache; rolls of heavy jowl swelling into an expanse of dark grey suiting which seemed to overflow the sides of his seat, narrowing down towards a pair of large, gleaming feet. The force of the man was tangible, filling the room as his vast body filled the chair.

'Good day,' said the walrus in a hollow dark voice with a hint of foghorns. 'And what can we do for you?'

'Excuse me,' I said, conscious of how small my own voice suddenly sounded. 'I'm Charlotte Hunter, your new pupil.'

'Ah, our new pupil.' From this majestic person the use of the royal plural, although unusual, did not sound in the least incongruous.

'Good. First class.' He bared a number of long, yellowish teeth. 'Welcome aboard, as they say.'

'Thank you very much,' I said, pleased by this hearty welcome. Mr Tobin might look peculiar but he seemed more friendly than I had expected.

'That's right,' Mr Tobin said. 'Just the job. Well now, let's see, first things first. Have you been to see Norman yet?'

Had I been to see Norman? For just a moment it crossed my mind that going to see Norman might be a chambers' euphemism for visiting the lavatory. I must have looked blank, for he went on, 'In the clerks' room; little feller there. Told you what's what, has he? Good, good that's the ticket. Well, I expect we shall be seeing something of each other in the months to come.'

'Yes, I expect so.' I agreed. We nodded in solemn unison.

'But for now I daresay a piece of advice wouldn't come amiss?'

'I'd like that very much indeed,' I said eagerly, feeling that in my present state of ignorance any crust or crumb of advice from anyone, let alone this magnificent man, could only be a benefit.

The walrus hauled his bulk upwards a little in the chair. 'Very well,' he said, as though I had asked him to oblige me with a recitation. 'I'll give you my little speech, the one I always give new pupils. I suppose it's two pieces of advice, in actual fact. Bear them both in mind and you can't go wrong.'

A silence fell – so long that I was beginning to wonder if I had had the pieces of advice and missed them, when he began again.

'The Law,' Mr Tobin said in a rhetorical tone, his voice if possible hollower than ever, 'is an unrelenting taskmaster. Are you married?'

'No, not at all.' I said, startled by this sudden turn.

'Oh yes, but you are.' He brought one fin down on the leather armrest of his chair with a loud flapping sound. 'Oh yes, you are, young woman. From this day forward you can think of yourself as married to – ' He paused impressively. 'The Law. Yes, the Law. Whenever she calls you must be ready to obey the summons. Is it a brief in the magistrates' court? You must rush off to Tower Hamlets or Clapham or wherever at a moment's notice. Is it an urgent request for further and better particulars? You must be prepared to drop everything. Is it a quick point of law? Then you must hurry to the library, whip out the relevant authorities and give an opinion at the drop of a hat. Is it an ex parte flying about over the road? You must be ready to nip over there and deal with it. Never a moment's delay; never a moment lost. "Speedy and deedy"; that must be your motto from this time forward . . .'

I listened in growing perplexity. Had the pinstriped strollers in the barristers' common room heard of being speedy and deedy? And, if so, when did they do all this dashing about which bore no resemblance to the idea I had had of the law as a dignified, rather leisurely profession? Also, it seemed that the undefended list was not the only unknown quantity across the road; there were ex partes flying about. What on earth was an ex parte and how was one expected to deal with it?

'And at night it's no more carousing for you.' He gave me a fierce and bristling look over his moustaches as though reading the signs of dissipation on my face. 'At night it's pleadings to be settled, affidavits to be knocked out, tomorrow's brief to be prepared. While others dally about with their mistresses, you must be the one with the wet towel wrapped round your head. At the ring of a telephone you must be ready to turn out and rush off at a minute's notice . . .'

He paused for breath or for effect. Had rhetoric carried him away or were there really people wanting a barrister at a minute's notice in the middle of the night? If so what for? Where would I be expected to rush off to? The walrus launched off a final blast: 'Yes, the Law is a harsh taskmaster. The Law is your mistress and your wife. You are no longer your own man, young woman.'

Seeming vaguely to perceive that there was something amiss with the conclusion of his speech, Mr Tobin covered any discomfiture he might have felt by clearing his throat with a loud barking sound. I was about to thank him when I realized that he had paused to consider.

'And the second piece of advice? What is that, do you ask? Well, here it is and note it well – ' He suddenly caught his chair a ringing slap with the other flipper. 'Always tie up one set of papers before opening the next.'

'Thank you. I'll remember that,' I said when it seemed that there was nothing else coming.

'Good show,' said the walrus cheerfully. 'That's the ticket.' Another silence set in.

'Um, excuse me,' I said finally. 'I was wondering if you'd like me to come in and sit down?'

'Delighted of course,' said the walrus politely. 'But in view of the time shouldn't you be thinking of cutting off next door to meet your pupilmaster?'

Somehow I got out of that room. Purple, I stood in the passageway outside trying to collect my wits. Put it behind you, I told myself; everyone makes mistakes. Mistakes perhaps, but a great thumping gaffe like that? It seemed unimaginable that anyone but myself could make such an embarrassing blunder within five minutes of arriving. I was still trying to put it behind me when something else occurred to me – something even worse.

I now had to face meeting Mr Tobin.

3

The door to the neighbouring room stood open. Not sure whether to knock, I stood looking in upon a scene of tranquil luxury. Edged with gleaming parquet, a Persian carpet clothed the floor with a silken mosaic of red and blue. One entire wall was lined with handsome books; floor-length velvet curtains framed a sweeping view of the lawns and the river on one side, the spire of the Middle Temple Hall and the rose gardens on the other. A crystal chandelier shimmered and turned gently in the morning sunshine. The room was dominated by an enormous mahogany desk topped with pale green calf heavily tooled in gold; the walls were decorated with fine old prints. There was nobody to be seen, but in the part of the room hidden by the door I could hear something going on. Interested, I stepped inside.

So awful was the devastation that met my eyes that for a moment I thought the room was being demolished. I gazed down in fascination on a raging ocean of paper. Along the wall was a huge antique table groaning under a weight of briefs so enormous that it had overflowed lava-like onto the floor. Every inch of the carpet over half the room was covered with papers in pink tape. A tiny girl with black hair drawn severely back into a ponytail and a young man with the face of a Dresden shepherd were beavering away in the midst of it all, each laden with an armful of briefs which they were throwing here and there about the room. It was like a postal sorting depot run mad.

'Phil, where's 1966?' the girl was saying as I came round the door.

'Under the table with 1967,' replied the boy, launching off a thin bundle with a practised flick of the wrist which sent it skimming across the carpet to fetch up against the leg of a brass-studded leather chair.

'Sixty-eight's here by my foot,' he went on, 'and wait a minute, oh lord, here's one marked 1963. Where shall we put that?'

'In the wastebin, I should think,' said the girl with a laugh. Her voice was surprisingly deep for one so fragile-looking. 'Oh hello, are you Freddy's new pupil? We heard you were coming this week. Welcome to the madhouse. I'm Lucinda Prior, Edward Jarrow's pupil, and this is Bill Armstrong's soon-to-be-former pupil, Philip Smyth-Endaby.'

'Phil,' said the young man. 'Hello.'

'Hello,' I said, pleased once again with my reception. 'I'm Charlotte Hunter. I was just wondering, actually, if this is Mr Tobin's room?'

'Yes, this is Freddy's hidey-hole,' Lucinda said, flipping the brief in her hand onto a stool. 'Have you been to see Norman yet? He should have told you where to come.'

'Well, yes he did,' I said, 'but I barged in on the wrong person, thinking it was Mr Tobin, I'm afraid.'

'You don't have to call him Mr Tobin, you know,' Lucinda put in. 'Everybody in chambers calls him Freddy.'

I knew of course that it was against tradition to call a fellow barrister Mr; it had to be either Freddy or Tobin. I decided that, of the two, 'Tobin' would be so hail-fellow and hearty as to be out of the question; so, however presumptuous it might sound, 'Freddy' it would have to be. I resolved as far as possible to call him nothing at all.

'Thanks,' I said. The girl smiled. Her face reminded me of a picture I had seen of a Spanish infanta. Oddly, she didn't make me feel uncomfortable, as small elegant people normally do. She was so – what was it? – fine-boned; not strictly pretty but effortlessly sexy and professional all at once in a cool black linen dress which displayed slender brown arms and neat little knees. Her tiny feet were exquisitely shod. This girl has class, I thought enviously; in a dress like that I'd look like the Great Smithfield Meat Exhibition. Suddenly I felt a shaggy clodhopper in my Bulgarian suit. I had been wrong: without exception, every small elegant person made me feel uncomfortable. Surreptitiously I gave my hefty skirt an upward tug from behind.

'What did the chap look like?' Phil's voice broke into my thoughts.

'Sorry, what chap?' I asked.

'The chap you walked in on?'

'A bit like a walrus,' I said without thinking. 'Oh, I don't think I should have said that –' But the others had burst out laughing.

'From that description it can only be Percival,' said Phil. 'Any offers for the Carpenter?'

'But who is Percival?' I asked.

'The head clerk.'

'No. I don't believe the man I met could have been a clerk. He looked far too, well – opulent.'

'What you mean is that he looked too opulent for a second clerk,' Phil said kindly. 'Did you notice a Silver Cloud parked outside? That belongs to Percival. Got a stud farm and a great place in the South of France, all from nothing. He's a great man is Percival.'

That had certainly been true enough. 'Still, I suppose he must work very hard for it,' I suggested.

'Well, he fixes the fees in heavy cases and goes to El Vino's to drum up trade. Oh, and does the *Times* crossword, I nearly forgot.'

'Tough,' Lucinda added. 'We're all in the wrong job, I sometimes think.'

'Then what does the second clerk do?' I asked.

'Norman?' Phil spun a heavy bundle into a corner. 'Everything else. You know, half the bar couldn't wipe their own noses when it comes to managing the practicalities. Without a good second clerk they'd be ruined men, helpless in the toils of self-employment. Take any example. A chap gets done for – let's say, dangerous driving. He'll go to his solicitor. Can't go straight to counsel and cut out the solicitor's charges because only a solicitor can instruct counsel, as you know.'

'Yes, but why is that?'

'Oh, it's laid down somewhere,' he said rather vaguely. 'Anyway, this solicitor would probably say, "You'll need a barrister to represent you in court. I'll brief Frederick Tobin's chambers because, even if he can't do it himself, the others are fairly competent." So he'll ring Norman and ask if Freddy's free to do the case. Norm looks in the diary, says Mr Tobin's too senior for the magistrates' court; Mr Armstrong's doing something else; will he have Mr Deacon? "How much?" says the solicitor. "He'll do it for twenty-five and two," says Norm – that's twenty-five guineas on the brief and two for the conference, of course.'

'What conference?'

'Hm. Normally means having a word with the client outside court.'

'Ah.'

'So the solicitor says his client can't afford that kind of money. Norm lays it on thick: would the client prefer Miss Pryor at three and two? The solicitor says he's talking about value for money, not the bargain basement . . .'

'Pig.'

'Just pulling your trotter, dear girl, no offence. Anyway after some haggling it's settled that Mike'll do it for twenty and two, shall we say. Norm enters it in the diary and the solicitor sends Mike the brief. After the case is finished Norm sends the solicitor Mike's invoice – called a fee note, for your information. The client pays the solicitor's firm, who put the money in a special account, and that's that. Norman's set the whole thing up, you see, leaving Mike to concentrate on the legal side.'

'When does Mike get his twenty and two?'

'Oh, I expect the cheque would follow in a year or so.'

'*A year or so!*' I was appalled.

'Mind you, by the time you take off ten per cent for the clerks' fee and take account of chambers rent, travel and so on, it'll be more like fifteen.'

'Ah?'

'. . . Gross,' he added darkly. 'Of course, I'm not saying things haven't improved since the old days . . .'

'How old? You mean since medieval times?' I could remember learning that the first barristers were noblemen who, rather than ask for a fee, would hang their hats over their shoulders in the hope that clients would stuff in discreet gifts from behind. In fact, a barrister's gown still has a hat stitched down the back – strictly for reasons of tradition, since any wearer who accepted a tip nowadays would very soon end up a snail-farmer.

'All that delay doesn't sound much of an improvement to me,' I said, depressed. 'Someone ought to make a stand about it.'

'What, bite the hand that briefs you? You must be joking. No, I meant things have improved since my father's time. These days, even a pupil can make a near-living. What my dad earned in his first year I wouldn't like to tell you.'

Before he could get the better of this reluctance, I remembered the list of briefs in my hand. Hopelessly I looked out over the sea of papers, wondering where to start.

'You won't find anything in this lot,' said Lucinda. 'Try the bookcase over there. Those are the briefs.'

I saw that the bottom three shelves were bulging with what looked like identical bundles of paper belted with pink tape.

'Er, what are these on the floor?' I asked.

'Papers,' she said. Then, seeing that I looked none the wiser, added, 'Briefs are papers which are ready for court. These over here still need something done. Here, you see.' She picked up one of the bundles at random. 'From Holt & Goodbody: "Instructions to Counsel to advise and settle Petition. October 1967 . . ."'

'But that's nearly two years ago!'

'Oh, that's nothing.'

'Don't solicitors get fed up waiting for the work to be sent back?' My image of Mr Tobin the stickler for punctuality had been rather shaken.

'Some of them do get a bit stroppy sometimes and ring up chambers and huff and puff,' she conceded. 'And then poor Freddy just has to roll up his sleeves and do some work, so everybody's cross for a day or two, but they keep coming back to Freddy because he's so good.'

'What sort of person is he?' I asked curiously.

At that moment the door flew open with a bang and something rushed into the room.

But it's a koala bear, I thought. Successful, professional and closely clipped though he looked, there was still a suggestion of fuzziness about the rounded lines of that shortish figure immaculate in dark wool suiting. Curly grey-brown fur-like hair receded from a high forehead, and on either side of a broad curving nose slightly protruding grey eyes looked out from beneath heavy lids with an expression both quizzical and shrewd. Nothing about this person could have been further from the saturnine figure of my imagination.

The newcomer came to a tearing halt inside the doorway and stared with almost comical dismay at the rising tide of chaos at his feet.

'Children, children, what on earth are you doing?' he demanded plaintively, raising one well-kept hand and waving it as if to sweep away the years 1965–8 at a stroke. 'This is quite appalling.

Where has all this rubbish come from?' His voice, which was not deep, had a curious timbre suggestive of pale grey velvet. 'You know what a stickler I am for tidiness. Get rid of it, for pity's sake.'

'Afraid it can't be done, Freddy. It's all your overdue paperwork,' Phil said in a ruthless tone. 'This week we're sorting it out for you in date order, starting . . .' he added rather pointedly, '. . . with 1963.'

A spasm of pain passed over my pupilmaster's face. 'Not in date order, my dear fellow, have a heart. I distinctly remember saying in order of solicitors if you absolutely must, but in any case not now; it's far too early in the morning. And besides,' he added rather contradictorily, 'it's late. Put it away now, there's good children. Playtime's over; we have work to do. Ah, wait a moment, what's this? It must be Charlotte? Good morning and welcome, dear Charlotte. How nice to have you with us.' He smiled. Although the word for the quality of that smile and indeed of the man himself was not in common usage then, it is not hard to recognize one-thousand-volt charisma. I found myself beaming.

'Thank you very much,' I said.

'Not at all. Mustn't shake hands in the profession.' My pupilmaster patted me kindly on the shoulder instead. 'Have you been to see Norman?'

I was becoming used to this question. 'Yes, I went there first thing. He gave me this,' I said, holding out the list. 'But I'm afraid . . .'

He took it from me. 'Excellent. Now, dear Charlotte, perhaps you'd like to start your pupillary duties by helping these abominable people to clear up their droppings. Quick as you can now.'

Obediently we began shovelling up the piles of papers and heaping them onto the table. My pupilmaster watched with an indulgent eye. 'There, that's better already, you see. An untidy room is the sign of an untidy mind. I can't bear mess. Oh, and while you're about it perhaps you wouldn't mind adding these.' Opening a magnificent calfskin briefcase stuffed to the brim with more paperwork, he emptied its contents onto the floor.

'Now what have we here?' He consulted the list. 'Let's see. Grummitt, Hardacre . . .'

Moving swiftly to the bookcase, he whipped half a dozen briefs off one of the shelves and dumped them on his desk. With the speed and dexterity of an expert fish-gutter he seized the first, slipped it free of the tape by bending the edged together, unfolded the contents and extracted the relevant parts, which he perused at extreme speed, murmuring to himself as he went. 'Petition, jurisdiction, good; children, none, good; discretion, yes; acknowledgement, confession statements, yes; good.' The papers were refolded, bent, retaped and dropped onto the desk as he swooped on the next, the whole process having taken less than a minute.

I watched with interest. This must be the period of concentration Norman had told me of during which he was on no account to be distracted. Indeed I do not believe he could have been distracted, for during the few minutes it took to gut the morning's work his absorption was total. He was, as I was to find, possessed of a formidable intelligence, much of which he devoted to the avoidance of tedium. Walking bored him, so he ran everywhere as though something nasty were on his heels. Paperwork bored him, so he did it either at rapacious speed or not at all. Entertaining and companionable; slumberous, brilliant; happy-go-lucky in nature, steely in principle: he was a man whose kaleidoscopic personality beggared description. He was rarely to be seen in the Temple without two or three pupils padding at his heels, and to each he imparted a sense of the combined reverence and irreverence which is life at the bar at its best.

'Now, young Hunter, my first words of advice to you are these,' my pupilmaster said, dropping the last brief back onto the green leather desk-top. 'As Confucius might have said if he had had more sense, never do yesterday what you can do today. Otherwise, you see, you run the risk of doing a great deal of work only to find on the day that you're doing something different. If there's one thing I can't abide it's wasted effort. Come along, children, it's off to work we go.'

In almost a single motion he swept the briefs up again, hooked the massive *Rayden on Divorce* from the bookshelf, swung his red wig-bag over his shoulder, and disappeared.

We filed through the door after him in a procession which grew ever longer as each time we passed one of the other rooms Freddy dived inside and rustled out its occupant. 'Here's the Queen's laziest Counsel asleep already, or is it still? Come along, David. Wakey-wakey, old boy; time to get up.'

A tall, languid-looking man lying full-length on a leather sofa put his head out from beneath a spread-out *Times*, folded it and slowly rose to join us. 'Good God, Freddy, don't roar like that. Feeling a little fragile this morning. Come to think of it, very much more than a little.'

'How was the circuit dinner?' Freddy asked.

'Good, as far as I can remember. Hello, who's this?'

'My new pupil, Charlotte. Young Hunter, David Jermaine, of whom you'd be best advised to be careful.'

I held out my hand from habit, remembering too late that barristers are not supposed to shake one another's hands. David Jermaine took my hand, kissed it and gave it back with a glance out of very pale blue and bloodshot eyes which made me feel that being a girl pupil might be rather exciting.

'He's a womanizer,' Freddy Tobin said dampeningly. 'Nothing in a skirt is safe.'

'Certainly not,' agreed Jermaine. 'Except Mrs Registrar Abrahams. Even I have my standards.'

'Out you come, Graham. Foot it featly here and there.'

A tallish younger member, introduced to me as Graham Webster, joined the group in a dignified manner. Through the open door a pale-haired older man hard at work at a desk by the window looked out, blinking like one disturbed from sleep. 'Shut the door, would you,' he observed briefly and took up his pen once more.

'That's Haliburton,' Jermaine said as the door closed. 'Chambers' probate expert.'

'Isn't he coming with us?' I asked.

'Heavens no. Never leaves his desk. Thinks everything else is a waste of time. He's one of nature's toilers.'

For a long time I found it hard to believe that Haliburton had any place in nature at all. He appeared to live at his desk and during my entire stay in those chambers I never saw him fritter away so much as a minute. Sandwiches were brought to Haliburton's room every lunchtime and the most frivolous event in his day would be a visit to the cloakroom down the hall. When I discovered that he had six children and another on the way I was amazed; but the knowledge that there was one activity at least which Haliburton did not consider a waste of time made him seem more human.

By the time we emerged into the sunbaked quadrangle and started up the Temple steps we were eight or nine strong. As we processed, Freddy, who was effortlessly in the lead, tapped on one of the ground-floor windows of a sooty-looking building on our left, then stuck his head inside. 'Come on, my dear Hulk. We are in need of entertainment this morning. David's feeling seedy, wants cheering up.'

'Heaven forfend,' murmured Jermaine behind me. 'What I want is euthanasia.'

There was a shuffling sound from within.

'He's on his way,' Freddy reported removing his head. 'What would we do without our dear old Temple Comedian?'

The Temple Comedian proved to be a towering man with a stoop whose clothes drooped from his large frame like a dust-cover. His face seemed set in an expression of gloom which the sight of us did little to lighten. Freddy greeted him delightedly and the two set off ahead, the long lank stride of one matched in syncopated rhythm by the swift steps of the other. I noticed Phil just ahead of me and came up to join him. 'Where are we going?'

'The Coffee Shoppe,' he said. 'It's breakfast time.'

The next moment we were filing into a tiny oak-beamed coffee-house to be greeted by the delicious mingled scents of toast, hot rolls and freshly milled coffee beans. Clearly, our group was regular, as a large table surrounded by low stools stood empty in a window bay overlooking a walkway outside, along which less fortunate members of the profession could be seen trudging to the station, bound for battle in outlying suburban courts.

'There won't be room for us all,' observed the Temple Comedian — over-pessimistically as it proved, for soon we were all squeezed somehow around the table, and steaming coffee cups with little pots of cream started making the rounds. I realized I was ravenous. I had been too nervous to eat at the start of this important day but now did full justice to the croissants – golden brown, flaky and fragrant, rich with butter, mantled with honey: a feast fit for the gods. And here I was among them, actually sharing a sugarbowl with those godlike beings whom as students we had watched from afar. Soon I was to hear what subjects these elevated people discussed among themselves. Fastening on a second croissant, I bent my ears to the snatches of conversation which came my way.

'. . . So then old Beasley said to me in that stagy way he has, "Alarse, Mr Crowe, these things are not as they were when you and I were young." It gave me a nasty turn, I can tell you. Silly old bugger must be eighty at least. "You and I" indeed! . . . The fellow's senile. That's it, go on, laugh. Heartless bastards . . .'

'. . . an odd little case where the respondent, it's alleged, regularly threw butter at the petitioner in the bath. Claimed it was at his own request, said he liked to be spread with marmalade. Could have been suffering from delusions – thought he was a bit of toast, I daresay.'

'Never eat butter myself,' observed the Temple Comedian. 'Knew a fellow once who ate a lot of fat. Fell down in court one morning, dead as a doornail, poor sod. Worst thing about it was that they'd set two whole days aside for the hearing . . .'

Owen Ap William, a soft-spoken Welshman with a reputation as one of the deadliest cross-examiners in the Temple, began a story about his previous day's case, punctuated by loud gusts of laughter from the company. Savouring the last of my croissant, I thought how lucky I was to be here. I had never expected to be made so welcome. I felt accepted, comfortable; I felt good. Over the rim of my coffee cup I caught the hot blue eye of David Jermaine looking in my direction. He grinned at me. There was no doubt about it: pupillage was turning out to be fun.

When I put my contribution of half a crown into the pool in the centre of the table, Freddy picked it up and handed it back.
'In these chambers,' he said, 'we never allow a pupil to pay.'

And indeed it was true. Months later I found my cheque for the hundred pounds fee normally charged by pupilmasters lying on my desk with a note attached: *Dear Charlotte, the pleasure was ours.*

Dear Freddy and Co., for the record, the pleasure was mine.

4

'My fur and whiskers, it's time we were off. Come along, young Hunter, time and tide . . .'

Swiftly Freddy gathered books, bag and briefs together, rose, dropped five shillings into the centre of the table and plunged out into the sun-dappled walkway. By the time I had drained the last of my coffee and squeezed out through the closely packed tables, he had darted up a dim passageway which led through to the Strand. I pelted along, regretting the second croissant, and managed to catch him outside the George Tavern, where the walkway emerged into a blaze of hot light. Across the busy Strand stood the Royal Courts of Justice in all its fairytale glory.

'That's the building,' said my pupilmaster tersely, reminding me of a film-style commando leader pointing out the objective of some desperate mission. 'We'll cross here.'

And we did. A moment's pause and we were off in a death-defying dash into the teeth of the traffic which had me thinking that, if I were spared, I would never do another wicked thing as long as I lived. Incredibly we fetched up unscathed on the other side and began a lung-splitting sprint along twenty yards or so of pavement, weaving madly in and out of the crowd, at times running along in the gutter. We had lingered too long over coffee, I thought, jumping over a small dog. Poor Freddy would get into trouble with the judge. I felt sorry for him. Whatever I did I must not delay him any more by falling behind. When at last I saw the massive portals of the entrance looming up ahead I could have kissed them.

Freddy ran to the top of the steps, where he halted and drew a handsome gold fob-watch from his pocket. 'Good, we've half an hour in hand,' he observed calmly, not seeming even mildly out of breath. 'I always allow myself plenty of time. If there's one thing I detest it's having to hurry, you see; it's totally against my principles and bad for the blood pressure. Are you all right, young Hunter? You look a little flushed.'

The best I could do was to nod.

'Also,' he went on, 'I find that when one is in a hurry things tend to go wrong. Have you brought your robes, by the way?'

I remembered that I had left my wig-bag at the Coffee Shoppe.

'Never mind, dear girl, we'll pick them up later. You've got a notebook? Never mind, I've got a spare one here. Now look after these a moment, there's a good child.' Piling the six briefs, *Rayden* and a clutch of notebooks into my arms, he bolted through a doorway to the left and was lost to sight.

I sat down on a bench. The interior of the vast hall was cathedral-cool and dim. The sunshine pouring in through pointed windows fifty feet or more above was diffused in the space beneath the dark ceiling-arch to a warm glow which filtered downwards as into a pool. The quiet was disturbed only by the soft click on the mosaic floor of the shoes of the passers-by, who moved constantly to and from the entrance, across the hallway, through doorways in the cloisters of grey stonework which ran its length on either side, and up and down the stone stairways beyond. It was very peaceful in this place where people came to do battle with one another. I had regained my breath and composure and was beginning to wonder idly why a huge building should be able to convey a deeper feeling of tranquillity than, for example, a hayfield, when I caught sight of Freddy in wig and gown returning from the robing room.

'Right, young Hunter, onward and upward. Mustn't lose any time.'

At these words I experienced a sense of foreboding which proved entirely justified. At breakneck speed Freddy darted across the hallway and up a steep flight of spiral stone steps. This led to a long gallery of courtrooms into which glass doors gave tantalizing glimpses of crested judges' thrones not yet occupied, wood-panelled witness-boxes, wigs abob on barristers' benches, and throngs of court personnel scurrying about in preparation for the day's work. Down four hundred yards of corridor we hurtled, past barristers in conference with clients, who glanced after us in mild surprise – round a corner, past Gothic archways leading to the unknown, in and out of a small thicket of pillars and down a flight of stairs. I am not a good runner but the prospect of falling behind and getting lost in that place, probably for the rest of my life, lent wings to my heels that day. We scrambled up some steps and down some more and suddenly we were out of the building altogether, shooting across an open flagway, into another building, along a short wind-tunnel, over a ramp and up three flights of stairs.

'Nice old place this,' Freddy called over his shoulder, making a bull-like rush at a pair of swing-doors. 'As the crow flies you know, the court we want is only twenty or so yards from the robing room, but the building was designed by an original mind and you'll find that getting from place to place is quite an intellectual challenge.'

I had by now decided that whoever designed this building must have been mentally deranged, but seeing Freddy's evident fondness for it decided against saying so and forged on with what I hoped was a smile on my face.

'Here we are, the Queen's Building.'

Through a pair of fire-doors that puffed together behind us we emerged onto a broad modern gallery in honey-coloured wood off which doors led to various courtrooms. The opposite wall was made entirely of glass; the summer sunshine streamed through with golden abandon, giving a curious effect of light without warmth, for the atmosphere was as dank and cold as a midnight bog. There was an overpowering smell of damp rubber flooring and somewhere a small chill wind was blowing. I shivered as prickles of sweat froze on my face and down my spine. I felt there should be toads.

'I'm not sure the air-conditioning is always quite properly adjusted yet,' Freddy remarked. 'You may not notice it here but inside the courtrooms it tends to feel a little damp.'

On a green baize noticeboard outside each court had been tacked a list of cases to be heard that day. We crossed the corridor and Freddy studied one of the lists. 'All listed not-before-eleven,' he said. 'And they've fallen behind with the list – only to be expected before Creeper Jones.' He raised his arms to heaven. 'Oh, Providence, why did you send us Creeper Jones? We'll be lucky to get away by lunchtime. How right we were, young Hunter, not to have hurried here.' He glanced through the pile of briefs and handed *Rayden* to me. 'Now, today we have a ladies' day: five wife petitioners and one husband.'

'How do you manage to remember one from the other when you have so many?'

My pupilmaster smiled. 'You'll find that, like everything else, it's largely a matter of practice,' he said. 'But by far the most important thing to remember, young Hunter, is that, although for us an undefended divorce may be no more than a few minutes' work, for the client it's different. A divorce is a big event in a client's life, as important as getting married and much more upsetting. These things should be treated with respect. Now you'll come across members of the profession, some even in our own chambers, I'm afraid, who will make it a point of pride to get through a simple undefended as fast as possible. You'll even hear talk of beating the chambers record. I need hardly tell you,' he went on severely, 'that that kind of attitude is thoroughly regrettable. Most clients need reassurance, building up; you could call it the personal touch. And if it takes a little more effort, that's what we're here for. Well then,' he eased himself more comfortably into his gown. '. . . Shall we go along and meet the first client?'

As I followed my pupilmaster's brisk footsteps across the squeaking new blue floor I felt sad for all those who had come here today to end unhappy marriages. The wife we were about to meet, for example: how must she be feeling now? Remembering her wedding day perhaps; thinking of the hope and happiness of that time and how over the years it had turned to sorrow? What sufferings had brought her here to see a chapter of her life ended in this impersonal place? I swallowed hard. Poor little woman, my heart went out to her.

Well, perhaps little was not quite the word. In fact, if that was our client in the corner there, the word was mountainous. She towered above her depressed-looking male companion, whom I took to be the solicitors' clerk, and her horizontal bulk was set off to merciless disadvantage by a pink dress out of which whitish flesh oozed at the armholes like meat from a sausage skin. Wiry black curls jutted aggressively from a square skull and a dark moustache shadowed her upper lip. As we drew nearer, I saw that she had the beginnings of a beard to match and her little blackcurrant eyes shifted here and there with a distinctly unwelcoming look. She was probably a genuine human being underneath, I thought. After all, she couldn't help her appearance. But then, neither could a Highland bull. I fell a pace or two further behind Freddy, glad that it was he and not I who had to deal with this client.

'Oh, Mr Tobin. Good morning,' said the solicitors' clerk in the tone of someone heralding the relief of a beleaguered garrison.

'Here you are, Mrs Grummitt, it's Mr Tobin,' he said to the client, adding rather superfluously, 'Mr Tobin's arrived. You'll be all right now, just you wait and see.'

I rather suspected that these last remarks were addressed to himself, for with obvious relief he sank down at a nearby table, folded his arms on his buff file and settled himself comfortably to watch Freddy go to work. The client looked down at Freddy, whom she topped by a head, and expelled air with a low hissing sound.

'Ah, it's Mrs Grummitt,' Freddy said. ('The one and only Mrs Grummitt,' his tone implied. 'The Right Honourable Mrs Grummitt.') He might have been waiting days, possibly years, to meet the client now looming over him. 'My name is Tobin and I shall be representing you this morning.'

From Freddy's manner of offering this relatively simple piece of information it would have been hard to say which of the two of them he believed the more fortunate. With a bland smile which somehow suggested great hidden depths of professional competence and intellectual power, he raised his free hand and effortlessly swept the woman into a chair, sat down opposite, laid down the six briefs and selected a notebook, murmuring gently all the while, 'No need to be nervous, dear madam, no need at all . . . nothing to be frightened of, nothing in the least . . . all perfectly straightforward . . . where did I put my pen? Ah, here it is. Comfortable? That's right. Good, good . . .'

The suavity and swiftness of this onslaught seemed to wind Mrs Grummitt completely. Unhurriedly Freddy unfurled the brief and found the divorce petition. First round to Freddy, I thought.

'Now the questions I shall ask you in evidence will be based on the matters set out in your petition,' Freddy said in his velvety voice. 'You'll find no difficulty about it.' ('Others might make an incompetent mess of their evidence,' his tone implied. 'But here is someone I can really trust.')

The corners of Mrs Grummitt's grim mouth seemed to relax slightly as she took in this masterpiece of diplomacy.

'Well then, we'll just work through the petition together, shall we, to give you the idea. I think you are Beryl Joan Grummitt?

Address as set out here? Good. Married 3 July 1956 to the respondent? And he is Alberg Grummitt? . . . Ah, I see, a typist's error. Albert Grummitt? Four children: Sharron Grummitt, Darren Grummitt, Vince and Dale Grummitt? . . .'

Swiftly and smoothly he whisked her along through two pages of questions and answers until they reached the part of the petition which listed the matrimonial misdeeds of the absent Mr Grummitt. The client drew in a harsh breath. 'He was a serpent,' she said violently with a shudder that set her spare tyres wobbling. 'Yes, a shark,' she added after a moment. 'Oh yes, Mr Tobit, I could tell you a hundred things which would make your blood boil.'

From the look of Freddy I thought this was being over-optimistic. Over the past few minutes I had noticed with some surprise that he was showing signs of sinking gradually into a torpor. His eyes, normally the only really animated feature in his face, were half veiled and had taken on a strange distant expression. He sat quite motionless and with each question the grey-velvet voice became drowsier and fell more quietly upon the ear. I wondered for a moment if he could have been overcome by the heat, but there was none. Outside the window the sun continued to blaze down but the atmosphere inside was like a misty morning in January. I could feel the chill beginning to strike through my clothes. Perhaps so much running had tired him out.

'. . . And I think there were violent arguments between you and the respondent?' Freddy murmured.

'Yes.'

'. . . Respondent would come home fighting drunk, shouting obscenities?' said the velvet whisper.

'That's right,' whispered the client, unconsciously lowering her own voice to match.

'. . . Smacked your bottom and bellowed insults in front of the neighbours?'

The client slowly nodded. It occurred to me that a man daring enough to smack the bottom of Mrs Grummitt must have nerves of steel. Freddy however merely inclined his head and made the gentlest of commiserating sounds: 'Tsk, tsk . . .In about 1966 attacked you with a clothes prop howling invective?' he breathed.

'That's right.'

'Tsk, tsk.'

I myself was beginning to find this behaviour very soporific. I sat up straighter in my chair trying to look alert and smothered a yawn. This was my first day in court. It would be disgraceful to fall asleep.

'. . . On an occasion in 1967, ran at you with a carving knife screaming threats to wring your neck?' suggested Freddy in a threadlike voice. The client managed to nod. ' . . .Waved a milk bottle at you in a menacing manner in 1967?' He leaned back and rested for a moment, eyes closed. ' . . .Called you a ropy old cow, also in 1967?' The pale grey voice was no more than a breath. 'Tsk, tsk.'

I felt my eyelids drooping and blinked rapidly. I must at all costs keep awake. Imagine this chair were on the edge of a hundred-foot drop and one second's loss of concentration would mean instant death . . .

'. . . In about 1968, when you accidentally slipped over in the road, called you a clumsy old bat . . .'

It was the merest faint ripple of a breeze in meadow grass, a long, long way off . . .

With a start I realized that Freddy's voice had ceased altogether. A silence lay over the table interrupted only by the relaxed breathing of the solicitors' clerk, who had apparently given up the struggle. Freddy was making notes. I looked across at Mrs Grummitt and saw that she showed many of the signs of a person in an advanced state of drunkenness. Her eyes followed my pupilmaster with the expression of a played-out cobra regarding a snake-charmer. The only person who appeared normal was Freddy, who finished making his note, replaced his pen in his pocket, bid a polite good morning to his collapsed client, saying that he would see her later in court, and set off at his usual relentless speed in quest of the next petitioner. When I glanced back at them, Mrs Grummitt's condition was unchanged and the solicitors' clerk had not regained consciousness.

'You see, it's as I was saying,' Freddy remarked cheerfully to me as we raced across the squeaking floor. 'It's no good rushing at a case like a bull at a gate. Take it steadily and you'll soon put solicitors and clients at their ease.'

During the next half-hour or so we seemed to see a great many clients. There was a dithery lady who kept bursting into tears and a stouter hearted wife who wanted Freddy to wring her husband as dry as a dishcloth. There was a ripe lady in a red dress who was having to admit to six adulteries of her own in a long statement full of such phrases as: 'I next unfortunately fell to temptation while under the doctor at Christmas 1967.' The husband petitioner was a small black man with a polythene bag full of holed socks which he insisted on having produced as evidence of his wife's poor standard of housecraft. It was a wide variety of clients, each with different problems, but in one respect the outcome in every case was exactly the same. As Freddy progressed down the corridor from one client to the next there were more heavy eyelids, more slumped shoulders; another pinched and anxious face the fewer. Afterwards, as we made our way into court, I examined the reception line of petitioners and was fascinated to see the same glazed look in every eye and a drooping head on every neck. It had been a truly remarkable morning's work.

I sat behind Freddy in court, watching the supple and assured way in which he dealt with one case after another and conscious of a feeling of personal inadequacy. I would never be able to do the job as Freddy did. For, even supposing that I managed one day to cultivate as impressive a court manner, I would never be capable of hypnotizing six people in half an hour.

'You may recall, young Hunter, my reminding you always to go by the golden rule . . .' Freddy said as we were on our way back to the robing room. 'Well, here's another piece of advice: always shove one brief well out of the way in court before beginning on the next. I rather think I may have done the same desertion twice. Fortunately nobody noticed. Ah, I see it's coming up for one o'clock. I think we might go over to the Cock and take a little refreshment, what do you say?'

We had crossed the road on our way towards this excellent objective when Freddy seemed suddenly struck by a thought which pleased him. A delighted smile spread slowly over his face. 'Young Hunter, that second adultery we did, you wouldn't happen to have timed it by any chance?'

'Timed it?' I asked, baffled.

'I made it three and three-quarter minutes. Three and three-quarter minutes, and before Creeper. Good heavens, this is going to cost someone a couple of drinks.'

He chuckled out loud. 'No doubt about it, young Hunter . . . it's a chambers record.'

5

That long green summer was a time of fascination. Each morning as I chased after my pupilmaster into the thick of the day's work I could be sure of adding to my ragbag of knowledge something interesting and new. We conferred with clients outside court, deftly extracting information and instilling confidence. Fair but firm, we compromised some actions and in others swept opponents down the drain by the power of advocacy. We addressed eloquent speeches to every kind of tribunal, to judges in court, masters in chambers, official referees hidden in the warren of rooms at the top of the Royal Courts of Justice, divorce registrars in the dark recesses of Somerset House. We took notes — or, to be accurate, I did. My pupilmaster did the rest.

When we were not in court, Freddy's huge table of paperwork gave me ample opportunity to try my hand at writing an advice or to grapple with the intricacies of pleading.

'. . . Here you are, young Hunter, look at this:

'. . . Further or in the alternative if, which is not admitted, the plaintiff sustained the alleged or any loss injury or damage the same was attributable either wholly or in part to the negligence and/or breach of statutory duty of the plaintiff his servants or agents.

'Simple you see, and to the point: that's what you should be aiming at . . . Now, you try it.'

After chambers tea at four, solicitors would arrive bringing lay clients for conferences and a day would often be well rounded off with a drink at El Vino's or the nearby Devereux. It seemed to me an ideal life.

The days slipped by until, incredibly, three weeks had passed and I had learned to settle a divorce petition and answer and three kinds of statement of claim, and to tie my bands properly at the front. In the evenings as I wandered home along the byways of northern suburbia, breathing the delightful mingled scents of tar and privet blossom, I would smile to think of the expertise I had acquired and what an ignoramus I had been so short a time ago.

Home, temporarily speaking, was the family house of Mr and Mrs Gossage: a big Edwardian villa standing in a shady garden at the back of Finchley. A cracked wooden board at the gate had painted on it the words RED MANOR STUDENTS' RESIDENCE – an odd title, since the house was built of yellow lavatorial brick; a grubby white elephant of a place raising a trio of trunks towards the city skyline.

I would have thought myself extremely lucky to have found accommodation here on the sudden remarriage of my previous landlady, had it not been for two particular skeletons in the hostel cupboard: Mr Gossage himself and the prospect of starvation. At mealtimes round the long wooden table in the basement the two spectres stalked together, amid much passing back and forth of large, near-empty serving-dishes and conversation along the lines of: 'Well now, whose turn is it for the extra bean tonight?'

On this particular evening somebody had taken a sprout too many, leaving me only two; the Vienna steak had been tough and the potatoes watery. I looked coldly at Mr Gossage. If it was not yet the winter of my discontent, the evenings were certainly drawing in.

'And how is our lawyer progressing?' Our host removed his executive horn-rims and polished them on his napkin. 'Has Charlotte successfully defended any murderers today?' He replaced his glasses and smoothed back his thick white mane with both hands in a boyish gesture which revealed several inches of black-haired wrist and a bracelet watch. 'We are all agog,' he added ironically, glancing at the dozen students round the table, all of whom at once fixed their eyes on their plates as though it had been announced that a sixpence was hidden in one of the boiled potatoes.

'Well, today I went to the Old Bailey to watch a rape,' I said to help the conversation along.

Mr Gossage raised heavy black eyebrows. 'One tends to wonder, I really must say,' he remarked, 'if the legal profession is the place for a young woman who wishes to retain her femininity.' His speech was cultured with a hard nasal undertone. 'Perhaps delicacy of mind in women is an old-fashioned ideal, but had *air* daughter chosen to be a lawyer . . .' He sipped his water reflectively.

'Hasan,' he suddenly pounced. 'Have you seen the Lord Mayor's Show? What, you have not? That is a great pity. What about you then, Nils? Have you seen it? Dear me. Marie-Claude, have you?' There was accusation in his tone as though he suspected that the ceremonial event in question had been carelessly mislaid by someone at the table.

'I do not understand you young foreigners at all,' he said loudly and slowly. 'You have all come from other countries to study air language and learn about air English way of life, and yet you do not try to find out anything about some of the old customs which are being carried on under your very noses.'

'My fader is e-seeing once a show in Strapford-Avon,' contributed a doe-eyed Persian boy.

'Ah indeed, Hasan? That is very interesting,' observed Mr Gossage pedagogically, adding for the benefit of the rest of us, 'Er, Stratford-Upon-Avon, as it should be pronounced, was, as some of you may know, the home of our great poet Shakespeare. What play did your father see, Hasan, do you remember?'

'I think my fader she see two, three toimes a streepy show. She say me, "Hasan, I enjoy too much these ladies but please not to tell your e-mader." I think she is froightened of my e-mader,' he added by way of explanation.

'Er, "he", Hasan,' corrected Mr Gossage, apparently deciding that the subject matter of this speech was best ignored.

'I am sorry?'

'You were speaking of your father. You should say "he said" rather than "she said". I am sure that you must have covered that by now in your language course?'

'Yes, thank you. That toime my e-fader he buoy in market of Strapford-Avon a noice e-dress, hoigh quality for my e-mader. When he give it to him, he loike that e-dress too much. He is wearing it too much in Tehran.'

'Er, Hasan, you were talking about your mother. We say, "She liked it very much; she wore it often."'

'Yes, thank you. My fader she buoy also in Strapford-Avon a trouser for my brother who is of woollen cloth, hoigh quality but too little between the legs. My e-sister is making him into a skirt. He was a factory sewer . . .' he added rather obscurely, 'in Strapford-Avon.'

'A factory sewer, Hasan?'

'Yes, sewing in factory. But now he is expecting a baby.'

Bored by the Strapford-Avon garment trade, Mr Gossage began turning a shrinking Thai student on the spit. Why had someone who so obviously despised all that was not English turned his house into, of all things, a hostel for foreign students? To supplement what he earned as an industrial embroiderer? What was an industrial embroiderer, I wondered. What did he embroider and for whom? Could he be secretly employed by the army, and if so to make what? Ornamental bomb-cosies? Saddles for regimental goats? I had heard that ladies' underwear could be made out of old parachutes. If this were his job, I reasoned, he might well feel sheepish about saying so. Perhaps he was forging antique samplers?

My speculations were cut off at this point as Mrs Gossage, a round brown woman at the foot of the table, began waving her lace handkerchief to signal to her husband that the meal was ended. With a scraping of chairs on the tiled floor the company rose and stood arrested in mid-action for grace.

'Lord, give us true hearts, sound thoughts and a good digestion,' demanded Mr Gossage, and dinner was over.

I walked out a prey to temptation. Resolutely I thrust it aside. I would *not* go to the Chinese takeaway. All that fried rice was making me fat. How was I going to catch a gorgeous pinstriped man when he came my way if I was round as a lobsterpot? Weren't we Hunters noted for our self-command, grit and reliability? When at last I stumped virtuously off to bed, little pink fillet steaks with sauté-potato wings flitted through my dreams, always too swiftly to be caught.

By a strange coincidence we were sitting round the table at the Coffee Shoppe the next morning when Mike Deacon asked to borrow a pupil for the afternoon. 'I've had Phil and Lucinda out on this matter before,' he said, 'but neither could come today and, frankly, I'm a bit stuck.'

'Have Charlotte if you like,' offered Freddy. 'I'm not using her for anything this afternoon. Where are you on anyway? The Court of Appeal?'

'The Dorchester. Conference with Gupta. She'll need a good appetite.'

Was I really being invited to the Dorchester Hotel? Would there be tea? Cakes? It seemed too good to be true and I wondered how Phil and Lucinda had been able to pass up such an entertaining prospect.

'Gupta,' said Freddy when I inquired, 'is a phenomenon. First, he is a keen admirer of young Deacon here. Sorry, dear boy, that might have been better put. The fact that he is, I think, certifiably insane in no way reflects, I hasten to say, on his persistent choice of junior counsel . . .'

'Freddy, this extravagant praise is embarrassing.'

'My dear chap, credit where credit's due. You see, this young Deacon holds a virtual retainer for a person – well, that may be stretching it – for a litigant who gets involved in so many lawsuits as to amount to a fairly busy practice in himself, wouldn't you say, Michael?'

'I'll say this much, Gupta's more trouble than he's worth. For sheer pettifogging, nitpicking aggravation that man is a . . . a horn of plenty. Last Sunday, Sunday mark you, he rang me at half past midnight to check the wording of a letter he was thinking of writing to the Prime Minister about his case. The man's got a maggot in his head.'

'The man is a maggot,' said David Jermaine. 'I saw him the last time he came to chambers.'

'I wouldn't deny there's a resemblance,' said Mike, much struck. 'If I had a pound for every rotten night's sleep that man . . creature's given me I'd be able to order a new suit, I can assure you.'

'Shame you haven't in that case,' remarked the Temple Comedian. 'Haven't like to mention it, but that getup you have on's a public nuisance in my view. No offence, old boy, but that green won't do. Look like a walking cucumber.'

'You need your eyes tested, Hulk. It's not green; it's called Hebridean Grey Heather Mix,' objected Mike, holding up one sleeve to the dim light from the walkway outside.

'Well, sorry to say the heather's gone mouldy,' said the Temple Comedian. Probably the Scotch damp.'

'Why's Gupta asked you to the Dorchester?' asked Freddy, tactfully changing the subject. 'Aren't chambers' tea and digestives good enough for him? I must say one hardly knows whether to feel offended.'

'Digestives may be all very well for the digestion but, according to Gupta, there's nothing like cream cakes for the brains.'

'Well, I suppose he never said there was nothing better,' Freddy remarked, reaching for the coffee pot.

'Hardly look as if you need feeding up, I must say,' observed Jermaine. 'No longer the whippet-like lad our wife married, are we, old bean?' He poked Mike in the ribs. 'A bit sprung these days, what?'

'Rubbish,' said Mike. 'There's nothing here that couldn't be got off by a few days' jogging.'

'Well, I should take out some insurance first,' said the Temple Comedian.

'He'd be better off paying Mike the money,' contributed Jim Harbutt, a beaky young man with a rampant mop of black hair.

'Fortnum's one week, the Dorchester the next, and all for what?' said the Temple Comedian. 'Where's the point in turning a perfectly reasonable barrister into a blasted lounge lizard? Quite green enough as it is,' he added with a sideways glance at the Hebridean Grey Heather suit.

Shortly after lunch Mike Deacon and I set off by taxi for the West End. In the bright heat of early afternoon the Strand had a Parisian air: brightly dressed strollers thronged the pavements and overspilled from every pub and sandwich bar to bask in the sunshine. The slow dusty river of cars ground through a ravine suddenly burgeoning with plants; ivy and canary creeper festooned the sombre stonework of building societies; office windows sported a brazen show of marigolds, red and pink geraniums and sapphire pendants of lobelia. Even the dark ramparts of the Charing Cross Station Hotel were brightened here and there by clusters of soft petunia trumpets.

Peering out of the window, listening comfortably to the sound of the taxi meter ticking up a bill I would not have to pay, I passed the journey to Trafalgar Square very enjoyably. My companion, however, seemed abstracted and sat staring in a depressed manner at his polished toecaps.

'The facts?' he said rousing himself when I asked about the case. 'Well, let's see, the history of this particular foul-up goes back to Christmas eighteen months ago when Gupta was voted off the board of his former wife's family company, having failed to grasp that the shares he'd filched from her over the years by way of letters purporting to make voluntary transfers had been registered by the company secretary, the ex-wife's uncle, as non-voting shares.' He gave a crack of laughter. 'You can imagine the pickle he got himself into when he turned up at the meeting with his cohorts of accountants all ready to take over the company, only to be told he had no voting rights. So qua plaintiff he's seeking reinstatement to the board and the reregistration of his shares as reclassified preferential shares.'

'Yes, well, thank you for explaining,' I said keenly.

'He is also,' went on Mike, 'the defendant in a consolidated action, being sued by the trustees of a family trust under which his former wife was the main beneficiary for misappropriation of several hundred thousands which were supposed to be paid over to his wife and ended up in his own back pocket. Gupta claims that as the husband he was entitled to the money under local law and the question of the subsistence of the marriage was also a live issue. So factually, you see, it's fairly straightforward.'

I was surprised by this last remark, having not yet encountered the lawyers' manner of grading the complexity of a problem. Anything less awful than the appalling mishmash just described, I was to learn, was 'perfectly straightforward'; the rest was 'fairly straightforward' unless so impenetrable as to deserve the ultimate term: 'a bit tricky'.

As Mike seemed to expect some comment I nodded in a slow and knowing manner and then, feeling that this might not perhaps be adequate, added, 'Wheels within wheels . . . It's so often the way, isn't it?'

For a nasty moment I was afraid Mike might ask the meaning of this gnomic utterance and I was surprised to find him in agreement with it.

'Exactly. Then of course the final seal was set on the whole shebang when the matter came before Pilborough, J., who partially ate my leader, tied old Gupta's ears in a bow round his neck and found against us all along the line. Dreadful.' He shook his head. 'So the purpose today is to see if any of the pieces can be picked up and cobbled together to make some form of viable appeal.'

'Do you think there's any chance?'

'There might be a run in it on one or two points, although personally I'm not particularly confident.'

'So what will you do?'

Mike turned a winter eye on the sun-dappled glades of St James's Park sliding past the window. 'I shall probably advise that we should get in a leader.'

'Sorry, do what?'

'Take the advice of leading counsel, a QC, as to the prospects of success on appeal. Gupta likes consultations with leaders; makes him feel important. Fortunately he can well afford it.'

'Out of his wife's back pocket?'

'Precisely so.' He got out his wallet, extracted two pound notes and held them out to me. 'Talking of that, I've just remembered: I must get to the bank before we start.' He tapped on the glass signalling the driver to pull in. 'When you get there, just carry on into the foyer would you, and hold Gupta at bay for a few minutes? Most helpful . . .'

'Yes, fine, but how shall I know him?' I asked, rather dismayed by this sudden delegation of duties.

'I'd say David was right on the whole: pretty well like a maggot in a short-sleeved shirt.'

'Yes, but er, maggots don't have much by way of facial features, do they? What's his face like?'

'Oh, that's simple. Basically like a pig.'

A few minutes later the taxi drew up outside the Dorchester Hotel. With a feeling of some apprehension I straightened my collar, pulled down my lace cuffs and pushed through huge revolving doors into the great sanctum. Sure enough, there in the centre of the lobby stood a small pink man and a large brown suitcase. Of the two I preferred the look of the suitcase. The man was absorbed in listening to a gold turnip watch which he held pressed to one ear. His face and body had been taken out of the mould before they were set and the exposed flesh of his bald scalp, neck and arms had an oddly naked look, like some newborn creature awaiting the arrival of fur.

I was able to approach quite closely before he noticed me, so preoccupied was he with the watch, which he in turns looked at, shook and tapped with a stumpy forefinger before squashing it against his ear again as if trying to embed it in the side of his head. As I neared him, he finally replaced the watch in his pocket and peered towards the revolving doors, pulling out a handkerchief and mopping himself copiously about the head and neck before stuffing it back into another pocket.

'Um, excuse me, Mr Gupta?'

He wheeled around and looked up at me in an aggressive manner out of pale little pink-rimmed eyes. 'Who asks please?'

'My name is Charlotte Hunter and I'm Michael Deacon's . . .' Michael Deacon's what? Messenger girl? Stoolpigeon? . . . Substitute? 'Michael Deacon's colleague,' I said, hitting triumphantly on the word. 'He's asked me to tell you that he's been detained for a short time but will be along in a minute or two.'

'I very much hope he will not be long,' Gupta said in a voice like a chainsaw. 'It is already 2.00 p.m. in the afternoon and we have much to discuss; much to do. I lean upon Mr Deacon entirely. Oh, forgive me, Miss er . . . I should say good afternoon.'

I grasped a hand which had the feel of warm tallow.

'Yes, yes, not a moment is to be wasted. We have many different courses to pursue.'

Suitcase in hand, he set off across the carpet looking alertly down at it like a foxhound scenting several trails at once. 'First things, however, first. Now that you have arrived, Miss er, I shall order tea. We shall sit.'

So saying, he sank into an armchair which was apparently deeper than he had anticipated for his little legs flew up into the air and I was hard put to keep a straight face.

'Tea,' he said when he had collected himself. 'That's what we want. Yes, by jove. With kegs.' He raised one arm in an imperious gesture which a waiter stationed by a nearby pillar gave no sign of having noticed. A frown stirred the flesh of Mr Gupta's brow. He smacked his palms together with a loud crack which resounded through the plush stillness of the lounge.

'Hi, you dawdling there! Yes, you, by jove. We want service please. Kindly present yourself here without delay.'

The buzz-saw tone of the command brooked no dispute. The waiter presented himself, but only unfortunately to bring disappointing news. Afternoon tea at this time? He was afraid not. The starting time was 3.00 p.m. The proper catering staff would then no doubt be ready to do what was necessary to provide refreshment should the gentleman still require it. Duty done, he had turned back towards the pillar when he stopped, arrested by a strange wheezing noise. I turned back too from the distant potted plant on which I had fixed my gaze in the hope of dissociating myself from Mr Gupta's imperious behaviour. Alarmed, I saw that he had turned clay-white; his lips had narrowed into a hosepipe, and beneath contorted brows his eyes glittered fiercely. He was beginning to breathe with a loud whistle and his toes were curling upwards. I had never seen anything like it before and thought at first that Mr Gupta was having some kind of seizure. I had just made up my mind to go in search of medical help when the whistling momentarily died away, and our client said clearly through clenched teeth, '*Tea*. With kegs. Or I will become really angry.'

'Yes, sir. At once,' said the waiter and ran for his life.

'That's the ticket,' said Mr Gupta breathing a little hard but with good humour otherwise apparently restored. 'Ah, with great relief I see Mr Deacon coming.'

Although I found this comment rather unflattering, I knew what he meant, for my own relief at seeing Mike Deacon entering through the main doors was at least as great.

'Ah, Mr Deacon, my dear fellow.' Mr Gupta rose in the grand manner and bared his fangs in a smile of welcome. 'Not a moment too soon, by jove.' He offered a melting handshake followed by what must have been intended as a hearty pat on the shoulder but owing to his lack of height turned into a thump in the kidneys. 'I have many things to show you so I must open my suitcase swiftly,' he said in the manner of a travelling salesman. 'Where are you? Where are you? Ah yes, I see you lying there behind the settee. If you will forgive me for a moment, Mr Deacon, I shall assure you of my closest attention in due course.'

With this he took a bunch of keys from his pocket, went down on his knees and began to grapple with the case. He upended himself and treated us to the sight of a pair of plump buttocks flexing and wobbling with the stress of his exertions. My view was obstructed but it did seem that the case gave as much punishment as it took, and there was a great deal of puffing and blowing before the lid flew open to reveal such a welter of loose documents that the wonder was that he had ever got it shut in the first place.

'By jove,' said Mr Gupta, rather flushed. 'Time to purchase a new suitcase, what?' He rubbed his hands together. 'Now let me recall where is the document I wanted Mr Deacon particularly to see. Where are you. Are you here? No. Are you beneath?' Like a fork-lift truck he began shovelling into the mass of documents. Rejected papers were tossed over his shoulder and settled here and there about the carpet.

Whilst Mr Gupta was so engaged the waiter returned carrying a large tray rattling with crockery and little metal tea and water pots with hotel crests and hot handles. A minion behind him bore a large platter of assorted cream cakes in frilly paper cases.

'Tea,' soundlessly whispered the waiter with a glance at Mr Gupta's back.

'Cakes,' echoed the minion. Then with one accord both turned like autumn swifts and skimmed back to the bowels of the hotel never to be seen again.

'Ah, good show,' said Mr Gupta, suddenly popping up and noticing the tea tray. 'Perhaps Mr Deacon would like to be the mother?'

'Might we ask Miss Hunter to pour?' suggested Mike, who was looking through a pile of notebooks laid out on a low table in front of him. 'I'm just trying to put my hand on a comment in the judgement which I think you ought . . .'

'Oh yes, our young friend, if she would be so kind,' said Mr Gupta sounding doubtful of my ability to perform this complex task. As I went through the ritual, it occurred to me that Mr Gupta might find the presence of a woman at a legal conference rather unseemly. Was that why he referred to me as 'our young friend', to gloss over the fact that I was a female? Rebelliously I fluffed up my hair and raised the hem of my skirt daringly almost to my knees. It was hot. I wished I could have taken off my jacket but could not remember if the blouse beneath was wrinkled and dared not risk it.

Mr Gupta now resurfaced with two or three papers which he handed to Mike. Reaching for the cake platter, he offered it ceremoniously. 'I'm sure our young friend will have a keg?'

His young friend certainly would. Greedily I scrutinized the selection. There were éclairs, sleek and elegant with cummerbunds of cream; brown-buttoned japonais and strawberry tartlets crowned with white piped stars; meringues like polar drifts; chocolate fudge cakes; pastries and primrose-pale custard slices dusted with nutmeg. To anyone who had stayed with the Gossages such a sight was pure perfection.

'That would be nice,' I said with gross understatement, taking the largest chocolate fudge cake and admiring its richly mantled outline.

'Good show. Come along, Mr Deacon. A keg?'

'Ah, thanks, Mr Gupta.' Mike scanned the platter and selected a slab of fruit cake.

'Right and tight. All serene,' said Mr Gupta briskly. 'So now you have cast your eyes onto the document, how do you see it, my dear Mr Deacon?'

'With difficulty, Mr Gupta. It seems to be in Urdu. What do you say it is?'

My teeth sank into the first forkful of cake. It was extraordinarily good: velvet soft and dark as dreams; a real collector's piece, as different from Mrs Gossage's bread pudding as feathers are from putty. By jove, I thought, idly brushing a stray crumb from the Bulgarian double breast, this was the life . . .

'What's this? "I give one hundred and three to Nusrat."? Again unsigned, I see. Mr Gupta, was there any notification of either of these purported transfers, or any registration? If you recall, this was one of the problems we had at first instance. Without notification there's no validity . . . Oh, yes I will, thanks very much, and I'm sure my colleague . . .'

This time I landed a large custard slice, a golden masterpiece lovingly enclosed by crisp pastry.

'. . . I'm also bound to point out, Mr Gupta, that taking these two documents into account we now have purported transfers of about a hundred shares more than your wife's actual holding. Well, of course, naturally, I accept everything you've told me, but I'm thinking of the court . . . precisely so. Now, turning to the broader issue . . .'

I was sinking into a torpor once again, enslaved by the subtle delights of cream filling and wafer-thin shortbread which made each bite an experience.

'Don't forget, Mr Gupta, that we're talking now in terms of the Court of Appeal, and I feel bound to tell you that there are quite a number of fundamental problems to be got over when you come to consider whether you wish to go forward . . .'

'I am dead bent, Mr Deacon,' cried Mr Gupta in his harsh voice.

'We shall and we will appall a higher court with this case. No problem. My mind is set up.'

'Before you finally decide,' said Mike carefully, 'let me just outline to you one or two of the considerations which are exercising my own mind . . .'

While he proceeded with this, I came to the end of the custard slice and put my plate aside with a sigh of satisfaction. It would have been a relief to undo my skirt button but since there was no prospect of getting at it through the Bulgarian jacket without a lot of vulgar scrabbling I made do with sitting up straighter and gave my attention to the conference.

'Next,' Mike was saying, 'the judge made certain findings of fact which unfortunately it is not open to us to overturn, one of which, now I have a note of it here, one moment, now where . . . Ah, yes. "As to the voluntary nature of any such alleged transfer of shares, I have great difficulty in accepting as truthful anything the plaintiff Mr Gupta has told the court –"'

'Libel,' snapped Mr Gupta, breathing hard. With alarm I saw his brows beginning to draw ominously together. Soon the hosepipe would appear. 'Nobody, not man, beast or judge, calls Nusrat G. Gupta a liar,' cried our host, fetching the table a smack which set the tea things loudly rattling. 'No wigged scoundrel plays fast and loose with me, by jove. Who will laugh last? I, the aforesaid Nusrat G. Gupta, will laugh when I look at Pilborough, J., . . . behind bars!'

The thought of this cheerful sight seemed to restore him to a calmer frame of mind. He swooped upon his teacup and emptied the scalding contents down his throat before turning to Mike a face from which all signs of stress had miraculously disappeared – a Jekyll and Hyde transformation which I personally found quite as unnerving as the original outburst.

'Come along now, Mr Deacon, have a keg.'

'Thank you, I'll have this fellow if I may, Mr Gupta,' Mike returned. 'I'm sure my colleague will be ready for another, too.'

'Ah, yes, our young friend. Another keg. Come along, come along . . .'

During the past quarter of an hour I had high-spiritedly gobbled down a japonais and a strawberry tart but was now beginning to feel that enough was enough. I looked across at Mike, who had been matching me keg for keg and was now getting ready to tuck into a chocolate éclair. Mildly surprised at his capacity, I shook my head. 'I couldn't, thanks very much. Enough's as good as a feast, as they say.'

Mr Gupta continued to hold the platter under my nose. I was about to refuse again but there was something threatening in the look of our host. I had already had a taste of what he could do by way of tantrums and was keen to avoid a second helping. So too, it seemed, was Mike, for he glanced at me in an expectant manner. I took a vast meringue and saw too late that it was sandwiched by a thick layer of cream to another the same size.

'I will tell you something just between the two of us, Mr Deacon, and the doorpost,' said Mr Gupta loudly and rather discourteously, I thought. 'I shall not rest until the abominable dessication of that judge is publicly rectified.'

I lost the thread of the discussion for a short time after this, for the meringue was extremely hard and I was having trouble preventing crumbs and fragments from shooting all over the carpet. Also, although a kind of in-for-a-penny bravado had carried me through the chocolate fudge cake, the custard slice, the japonais and the strawberry tart, I was now beset but pangs of guilt as to the effect of all this stuffing on my shape. What if here and now all that excess suddenly turned to flesh and mantled me unrecognizably like a chocolate fudge cake? Already I could feel my skirt getting tighter. Didn't my left calf look stouter all of a sudden? Like an oak-trunk, no doubt; I hardly dared look down, especially as my feelings of queasiness was now not only mental but physical.

'I am very satisfactory, Mr Deacon,' our host announced, 'to know that we are united in our desire to proceed forward, by jove. I do not hesitate to give you the good news that we shall have much future business, whatever befall us next in this matter . . .' He ticked them off on podgy fingers as if listing forthcoming attractions on a variety bill: 'Property disputations; an action upon the tort of nuisance; two claims against London Borough of Wandsworth involving many damages; and above all, Mr Deacon, I intend to proceed forward in the magistrates' court for criminal libel, against Pilborough, J., no less. Pilborough behind bars! Your name, Mr Deacon, will be in the Hall of Fame. You look grave, my dear fellow, but we should celebrate. Have a keg.'

'Ah, I may just permit myself this chocolate slab,' said Mike unbelievably. 'I notice my colleague also has an empty plate.'

'I'm afraid I really couldn't . . .'

'My good young friend, permit me to insist . . .'

'No, really, they were lovely but . . .'

'Well, Mr Deacon, I am afraid your colleague has left you carrying the baby, so to say,' said Mr Gupta with an edge to his voice. 'You know how it would distress me to leave any kegs behind. Our meeting cannot end, my dear fellow, until the plate has been eaten away. I must insist.'

In a flash I realized why I had been brought here: I was an eater. My job was to help Mike Deacon chew his way through a conference which might otherwise last all evening. Yes, he was relying on me to help and I would not fail. I'd show what we Hunters were made of or burst in the attempt. With a stiff upper lip I reached out and took the last cake.

Mr Gupta meanwhile set about the monstrous efforts needed to repack and shut his suitcase, which included a good deal of bouncing about on the lid. I averted my eyes. The sight of that doughy form flopping up and down was more than I could stomach. At last Mike rose to take his leave. Somehow I also got up. My insides were churning like a washing machine and waves of carpet rose and rolled about me like ocean swell. Mr Gupta appeared to be holding out three hands.

'My dear Mr Deacon, a pleasure as always, and as always an illumination upon my affairs. I am delighted the tea was satisfactory,' he said in response to Mike's thanks. 'You know, my dear fellow, I have so often thought that you should spend a whole weekend here as my guest. We would reside in my suite and work together towards the consummation of my interests. Examination of the documentary evidence, sorting, sifting . . .' He nodded towards the suitcase. 'Think what could be accomplished. Come, come, what do you say?'

'I'm sure my colleague would be only too happy . . .'

I rocked away to the ladies' room without pausing to find out if the words were real or the product of my feverish imagination.

'Well, I hope you'll allow me to compliment you, Charlotte,' remarked Mike in the taxi back to chambers, 'on the sheer number of cakes you managed to eat. I don't think I've ever seen anything quite like it. When you said you were being starved at that foreign hostel place you weren't kidding, were you? I must say, on any showing it was an achievement. How did you do it?'

'Oh, I don't know,' I said modestly. 'We Hunters are noted for our self-command, reliability . . . grit . . .'

'I'm surprised you aren't noted for your enormous size if you all ship food aboard at that rate.'

'Well, you ate as many as I did,' I reminded him.

'Ah,' said Mike Deacon. 'I haven't represented Gupta all this time without learning a thing or two.' He dug in his pocket, produced and unfurled a crested napkin and offered the seven cream cakes inside with leering panache. 'My dear young friend . . . have a keg. I say, Charlotte, you've gone a bit green. Are you all right?'

6

'You know, you can say what you like . . .' said Graham Webster.

'Can I really? Good,' said Jim Harbutt. 'Well then, with all due respect – cobblers.'

'I say, steady on,' said Graham rather affronted. 'I don't know why you say that.'

'I say it, Webster, because you're handing me out a load of utter and complete balderdash, again with respect. Good lord, if I only appeared for clients I entirely believed, my practice would topple from its present pinnacle of mediocrity straight onto the scrapheap. I'd be doing eighty per cent less work at least. Scratching a living at the Bar's hard enough, you know, without trying to live up to impossible standards.'

'I don't know why you say a readiness to give some room for doubt is impossible,' objected Graham. 'All right, I'll grant you that if a client said to you, "I in fact committed the robbery but I intend to argue that I was a hundred miles away at the material time and I want you to put that forward as my defence," you'd be justified in taking up a sceptical standpoint –'

'Sceptical standpoint be damned. If a client said any such thing I'd have to decline to represent him unless he pleaded guilty, as you well know. A poor example, Webster.'

'Yes, but, as I was going to say, unless he actually comes out and makes some such admission to you, there must ex hypothesi be doubt and you owe it to your client to give him the benefit of that doubt.'

'Absolute cobblers, with due respect. I owe my client to look after his interests and put forward his case to the best of my ability, and I can do that perfectly well whether I believe him or not.'

'With respect, I don't agree. To my way of thinking an advocate can only put a case forward with conviction if he actually has faith in his own arguments, otherwise the whole exercise is hollow. Nothing personal, I hasten to say . . .'

'Do you mean to say you personally believe every client you represent?' I put in.

'I think I can say that I do,' said Graham judicially. 'Even if I start off doubtful, I generally find that by the time I've put together all the arguments in their favour I've somehow convinced myself.'

'A very loose and woolly approach,' remarked Jim. 'Allowing your logical faculties to be pulled this way and that by your own arguments shows a mental flabbiness which does not become you. It's only by preserving complete detachment that one can see a case in its true light. If you can pick out the weak points in your own case from the word go, you can put up a much more effective showing. I'd almost say that as a matter of mental discipline I made it my business to remain sceptical of anything I'm told by a client.'

'That sounds more than a little cynical, if you'll excuse me,' said Graham looking by now somewhat pink and ruffled.

'I'd rather be a cynic than a flabby-minded romantic.'

Breathing rather hard, the two faced each other across the table.

'. . . With all due respect, naturally,' concluded Jim. 'Here, can anybody see a green pencil?' He began patting the surface of the papers strewn across his desk with the flat of both hands. 'It's got to be here somewhere.'

'Look behind your ear, if you can find it in that mop. That's where you always put pens and pencils and I wouldn't know what else.'

'I can't recall a single occasion . . .'

'You invariably forget you've done it.'

'Well, I certainly haven't this time.'

'. . . And then swear blind you haven't.'

'Nonsense. Absolute rubbish. Slander.' Jim dug questing fingers into his springy black poll of hair and after a short time drew out a red biro. 'Good lord, you're right. Well, I must say, I'm at a loss to account for that. It shows you the depth of my concentration though, doesn't it?'

'What it shows, Harbutt, is bad habits and a worse memory. Here, have some of your overspill back.' Graham pushed a stray affidavit over the edge of his own tidy desk into the adjoining chaos of Jim's, where it disappeared.

The room shared by the two most junior tenants in chambers

was a converted broom closet only just large enough to contain a few bookshelves, three straight-backed chairs and a wastepaper basket. A single window looked out across the lawns to the river, and it was presumably to share this view that the room's occupants had taken the unusual step of joining their desks together to form a table in the centre. This always struck me as odd – not so much because they spent so much of their time arguing, which they could have done from wherever they sat, but by reason of their completely different methods of work.

Graham was a silent worker. He did not puff or mumble. When he wrote his pen did not squeak. His paper did not crackle. Soundlessly his hand travelled back and forth across the pages, leaving a wake of neat script. The wild and wiry Jim, however, attacked his paperwork with such ferocity that his desk shook and creaked beneath him. Papers rose and floated off; books plopped over the side to be retrieved with irritable heavy breathing and thumped back onto the scene of operations. To see the two of them simultaneously at work made me think of some unlikely joint venture between an electric shaver and a threshing machine. A by-product of Jim's exertions was a creeping disorder which slowly overflowed onto every available surface. When high tide was reached, Graham would suddenly become aware that he was working on a tiny corner of his own desk and with the ease of long practice would shovel the lot back over the boundary without even raising his eyes from his papers.

This forbearance was at least matched, though, by Jim's willingness to put up with Graham's speeches. He liked to rehearse these while waking up and down in the narrow space between the desks and the window, making strange hand movements like a person conducting a soundless orchestra, possibly under the sea. Sometimes, when carried away, he would accompany the semaphore with disjointed mumblings, occasionally whacking his palms together for emphasis:

'. . . The petitioner's . . . bum, bum, bum's all very well as far as it goes . . . but does it go far enough? What do I say to that? I say, bum, bum . . . smack. But that's only one side; what about the other? To that also I say, bum . . . smack, bum . . . smack . . .'

'Have you and Graham always shared a room together?' I asked Jim once, curious to know how they managed without resorting to murder.

'Well, before Graham joined chambers I used to share a room with Mike Deacon. Nearly came to a sticky end that, as a matter of fact.' He shook his head. 'A good chap Mike, but, you see, he has this frightful habit of bending paperclips . . .'

'Well, well, I suppose I'd better get to grips with this reply and defence to counterclaim.' Jim had just rolled up his sleeves as though getting ready to take four or five rounds with the thing on the carpet when there was a hasty knock on the door, which flew open to admit Norman. He came in at a run carrying a large brief which he dumped in front of Jim, saying without preamble, 'Inner London, sir. Return of Mr Deacon's. Young Paul missed it in the diary. Court's just been on the line; they've been waiting since twelve for Mr Deacon, according to the listing office.' Overcome by this dreadful thought, he pulled out a handkerchief and mopped his face.

'Where is Mr Deacon?'

'Devizes,' said Norman, showing signs of barely repressed hysteria. 'Court four; defence brief for Shaw's. I've told the court you're on your way now, Mr Harbutt, so off you go, quick as you can. Oh, you might like to take Miss Hunter here with you?' He spoke as though offering a person about to face a firing squad a lucky rabbit's foot. 'Well, off you go, sir,' he said again, pointing at the pile of papers several inches thick on the desk. 'I expect you'll have no trouble getting outside the brief in the taxi. Stand yourself a taxi on this occasion, I should.'

With characteristic smoothless Jim Harbutt swung into the breach. 'Yes, all right, Norman, leave it with me; I'm going, I'm on my way now. Bugger it, where's my briefcase? Sling over that *Archbold*, would you, Graham? You've got no idea what it's all about, I suppose? A fight? Well, obviously. Where's my notebook? Bloody hell, where's my biro? . . . Somewhere in all these . . . papers . . . Oh, thanks, Graham. Got my wig-bag, Charlotte? Good. Better ask Freddy if you can come; I'll meet you in the clerk's room in two minutes. All right, Norman, I'm going, I'm going . . .'

His voice followed him down the corridor as he sped towards the clerks' room, crumpled paper book-markers swirling from his half-open briefcase to lie like shed feathers in his wake.

'Right, let's have a look at this.' Jim humped his baggage onto the floor of the taxi and himself onto the seat. 'Let's have the tape off; there we are. No time to read the prosecution statements now; we'll have to piece it together. Here –' He thrust the backsheet at me. 'Have a look at the instructions and let me have the salient points while I find the defence statements. Here's the indictment. First of all, what's he charged with?'

'Wait a moment: one count of burglary and one of going equipped. It is alleged that he was involved with two others in breaking into a shop. One ran off, the other's pleading guilty; so your man's the only one fighting.'

'Right. Are the facts set out in the instructions?'

'Well, it says here:

'Mr Macaulay's defence to the charges is somewhat difficult to ascertain. He has provided a number of statements of which instructing solicitors believe the most recent to embody the current defence.

'As to his original statement in which he claimed to have been playing pool in Peckham during the whole of the night of the burglary, instructing solicitors reminded Mr Macaulay of the police claim to have arrested him at the scene, to which he made the comment that that must have been his brother.

'What does it all mean, do you think?'

'It means our friend's lying through his rotten little teeth,' said Jim succinctly. 'Look at these.' He handed me two sheets of paper, the first of which read:

'MICHAEL MCGINTY MACAULAY, unemployed labourer, of 42a Mill Lane, Catford, WILL STATE:

'On a night last December I was out walking the dog when I remembered it was my gran's birthday. I decided to drop in and wish her many happy returns. When I left her place it must have been about 2.30 a.m. I happened to go past a shop with some bother on the roof. I had stopped to have a look when police rushed up and arrested me. There may have been seven or eight of them. I asked what I was supposed to have done but received no reply.'

I turned to the second sheet of paper, which was similarly headed. This said:

'On the night of my arrest I had gone to bed when I had a telephone call from my brother-in-law saying that he had trouble with his roof leaking and needed tools. I set off at once with the tools and was passing through Peckham when I remembered it was my gran's birthday and decided to drop by and wish her many happy returns. When I left there it was about 2.00 in the morning. On reaching my brother-in-law's house I climbed up a pipe onto the roof to help him only to find that I was on the wrong roof. Police then rushed up and arrested me.'

'But neither of these statements is dated,' I said in dismay. 'How are we supposed to know which one is his latest defence?'

'Oh, I shouldn't worry; you'll probably find he's thought up a completely new account while on remand,' said Jim. 'Someone inside may have given him a few new ideas. I know his kind – no good expecting to find out his defence for sure until we see him. If then,' he added wryly.

'Er, Jim, all this changing of his story – doesn't it make you just the slightest bit suspicious?'

'Suspicious of what?'

'Well, that he might . . . well, I don't want to prejudge him or anything . . . but that he might have in fact committed the offence?'

He looked at me in surprise. 'I should have said there was no doubt of it whatsoever, wouldn't you?'

'But surely it makes some difference?'

'Why should it? I'm not the jury, nor are you. It's not our job to decide if he's guilty or not, thank God. We're there to find out his latest defence and put it forward in as convincing a manner as possible, purely and simply. And all I can say is,' he said, picking up the defence statements and putting them back together with the brief, 'I hope he's thought of something a bit stronger than this old load of claptrap. Any juror who believes a word of these needs his head examined. Oh, and by the way, I shouldn't ever refer to a client's "story" if I were you. It tends to suggest that you don't quite believe it yourself. The better word is "account". Oh look, we're nearly there.'

I was still turning over in my mind the shockingly bald cynicism of this outlook when the taxi pulled sharply across the road and in through a pair of stone gateposts where stood a distinguished-looking grey building smothered with scaffolding. The forecourt was a waist-high jumble of builders' debris full of men in orange helmets working like ants. During a career which brought me to this particular court on many other occasions, I grew fascinated by the interminable works which seemed over the years to take on the nature of a permanent exhibition of building techniques. One week a complex of wind tunnels would snake round the carpark; the next it would be smart portable cabins with orange walls and real glass windows. Sometimes in the winter there were huts with glowing charcoal braziers; on other occasions the way to the outlying courts would be cut off by hoardings bearing notices ordering us all to report to the site foreman.

On this particular afternoon, still politely shouting back and forth about the proper size of my contribution to the taxi fare, we walked – or rather ran – the plank across a number of pipe-laid ditches and vaulted a small barricade of cones before reaching the stone steps leading up to the main concourse.

'Quick,' puffed Jim. 'Women's robing room's there somewhere. Court four, soon as you can.'

He sprinted off down the corridor and was gone.

The huge old-fashioned robing room was all wood and green leather. There was even a chaise longue – upon which to collapse, I supposed, after an unsuccessful court appearance. It was very quiet. All the women must be in court, for there were three or four wig-boxes on the table: shiny lozenge-shaped tins lacquered in ebony black, each with the name of its owner painted in gold lettering on the lid. As quickly as I could, I shook my own wig from my bag onto the table and fumbled it free of the protective folds of my gown. Coiled like a serpent under the wig lay my old adversary the wing-collar, greyer now but still able to deliver a stealthy whack in the eye. Urged on by the need for speed, I ignored this and the odd low blow about the adam's apple and secured it with surprisingly few duff shots – only to find that I had somehow mislaid half the hairpins needed for the beetle knob. I found a piece of twine in my handbag and managed to improvise although the result was bristly and so aesthetically queer that, as I caught sight of myself running from the room, still with one red and half-closed eye, it struck me that all I needed was a broomstick.

I reached court four to see the lone thin figure of Jim emerging. In his black gown, hunched forward with hands in pockets, he resembled an irritated rook.

'Shaw's haven't turned up,' he observed bitterly looking round the empty passageway. 'If they'd sent someone this morning, even the usual fifteen-year-old filing clerk, she'd have had the wit to realize Mike wasn't coming, got on the blower to chambers and all this hassle could have been avoided. Typical Shaw's: lie low and let counsel take the rap. Typical solicitors,' he added rather unfairly. 'Damn and blast. If old Judge Lightfoot gets wind of the fact that they're not here, he'll haul up their senior partner and chew his head to wood pulp – and that'll be the last I see of Shaw's. No, there's only one thing to be done, Charlotte: I'm afraid you'll just have to get your things off.'

'What?'

'Yes, be as quick as you can. The judge'll be coming back any minute.'

'What do you mean, get my things off; how many things?' I asked suspiciously.

'Oh, disrobe completely. You can leave everything out here. I'd better go in. You can come in when you're ready.'

'Come in and do what?' I asked, wondering about the lengths to which I was being asked to go to distract the judge's mind from the absence of an instructing solicitor.

'Sit behind me of course. Here, stick these papers on the desk in front of you and try to look as much like a solicitors' clerk as you can . . . Twiddle your thumbs a bit.'

With this acidulous comment he handed me a bundle of statements and went back into court. I took off my wig, gown, bands and collar and put them on a bench outside the doors. Then I entered the court and slid into place behind Jim on the solicitors' row. To stand, or more accurately to sit, in the shoes of the absent filing clerk was promotion indeed. It was a pleasant change to feel useful.

A loud bellow from the usher announced the appearance on the bench of His Honour Judge Lightfoot, a man with the physique of a potato sack and a dusty purplish complexion which suggested high blood pressure. Jim rose and in a strong and wide-ranging speech apologized for the inconvenience to the judge and the wasted time of the court, directing his comments to counsel for the prosecution, witnesses, jurors-in-waiting – everybody, it seemed, except solicitors and their clerks, although this may perhaps have been an unintentional oversight. Everyone concerned, he said earnestly, would now do all within their power to ensure that there was no further delay for any reason whatsoever. In reply, the judge confirmed that the whole sequence of events had been nothing short of lamentable. If need be, the court would sit until nine o'clock that night to make up for the time thrown away. The plea would be taken forthwith, the jury empanelled as quickly as might be, and the trial pushed forward with all possible speed. The clerk, prosecuting counsel and some of the keener jurors-in-waiting were still nodding their agreement with this rigorous programme when Jim got up again and asked for an hour's delay to enable him to take instructions from his client.

There was a nasty silence. The judge turned rather a bad colour but after a few moments, when I had begun to wonder if he would spontaneously ignite like a Christmas pudding, he unexpectedly announced that he was prepared to rise for ten minutes – but, be it noted, ten minutes only. A loud cry from the usher announced his departure from the bench.

'Come on,' said Jim, and bolted from the courtroom, across the concourse, down a flight of stairs and along a passageway at the end of which was a heavy locked steel door with a small peephole. Beside the door was a bell which Jim had to press a number of times before a large magnified eye could be made out rolling carefully round us.

There was a further wait before we heard the sound of keys being selected and inserted; the door swung silently inwards, revealing a large and cheery-looking police officer in his shirtsleeves who said he was sorry to have kept us waiting but there had been a bit of bother about a prisoner who had been left behind at Wandsworth, causing the judge to do everything short of laying an egg. He supposed the powers-that-be expected him to wave his magic wand. Could we see who? Macaulay, full name Michael McGinty? The policeman scratched his head vigorously as if to stir up the mental processes beneath and said that he could recall nobody of that name. He wouldn't take his oath that there wasn't a Macaulay down from Brixton but on the other hand he couldn't swear that there was. He would look at the list of re-mand prisoners. Slowly he went away. Jim looked at his watch and sighed through gritted teeth. After a time the officer came back to say that unfortunately he rather fancied that the list had gone missing. One of the other officers might have misplaced it; he rather thought that officer was up in court. Would we like to hang on a few minutes? Ah, it was a matter of urgency; time was of the essence, was it? Ah.

The officer stood for a moment looking at Jim in a speculative way, perhaps wondering if he too were about to call upon him to wave his wand. 'Ah,' he said again. '. . . Well,' and, filling his lungs, bellowed, 'Speak up, Michael Macaulay! Michael Macaulay, speak!' in a stentorian voice which echoed round the cell block and was answered by a faint 'Here' from further down the passage. We started walking.

'Michael Macaulay, speak up again!'

'Here.'

'Where?'

'Here.'

'Oh, there you are. Here's your briefs come to see you, Macaulay,' said the policeman. 'Do you want a consultation room or will here do, sir? I could go and see if there's a room free . . .'

'Here will do fine, thanks.' Jim looked at his watch again.

'Right you are, sir.' Having unsuccessfully tried a series of keys, the policeman carefully unlocked the cell door and ushered us into a small dark space. There was a reek of urine, carbolic and stale cigarettes.

'Knock when you're ready, sir.'

The policeman locked the door and padded away, leaving us in the presence of a man sitting hunched on one of the two benches with which the cell was furnished. From his posture I took him to be old and was surprised when he rose and revealed himself to be no more than twenty: a sad, shambling figure; pale, with carroty hair sticking up like wheat stubble from a ballpoint of a head.

'Well now, Mr Macaulay,' Jim said when introductions had been made. 'I fear our first meeting is likely to prove rather short.'

His fears were immediately confirmed, for at that moment the door swung open again and the policeman reappeared. 'Case is being called on, sir. Come on, Macaulay, this way.'

Almost before it was clear what was happening, the young man was whisked from the cell and marched off between two officers. Robes flying, Jim raced off in pursuit and the two heads, one bristly, one curly grey, bobbed along together as the rest of the conference took place on the move between the cells and the court. From the rear of the procession I watched them reach the top of a flight of steps and pass out of sight. A moment later I came up through a kind of trapdoor to find that we were all milling around in the dock: the two officers from below, a pair of counsel, two dock officers and Mr Macaulay, who had he thought of it could, I am sure, have slipped away and made good his escape in the confusion.

'Did you find anything out?' I asked as Jim and I made our way towards the junior counsel's and solicitors' rows respectively.

'Well, of course he'd forgotten what he'd put in his statements. I read them out to him; he agreed with both although they're inconsistent, and that was all there was time for. I'll just have to apply for further time; this is quite ridiculous. I can't possibly present the case properly without a thorough conference.'

'What if the judge won't give any more time?'

'I shall put my foot down; that's all there is to it.'

A bellow from the usher announced the reappearance of the judge, who strode onto the bench in a flurry of mauve silk.

'What, another adjournment, Mr Harbottle? I hoped I had made it clear that I am not prepared to countenance any further timewasting,' the judge shouted with furious incredulity, as though Jim had suggested a picnic in the well of the court. 'Let the accused be arraigned forthwith. No need to remain standing; you may sit down while the charge is put, Mr Harbottle,' he added, taking all remaining wind from the sails of Jim, who, while still on his feet, appeared temporarily to have lost control of the situation. 'We shall all of us pick up the case as we go along, I have no doubt.'

As the jurors came up to take the oath, Jim scanned each carefully, alert to challenge anyone who showed unsuitable tendencies, such as a rolled-up *Daily Telegraph* or a bowler hat.

'Have a word with Macaulay, could you?' he whispered. 'I want to know at least whether we're running the dog, the brother-in-law and his roof, or grandma.'

Obediently I got up, bowed to the judge and went back to the dock.

'Excuse me, Mr Macaulay, on the evening of the burglary did you go to see your granny and your brother-in-law?' I whispered.

'Yes.'

'. . . Or just your grandmother?'

'That's right.'

'Er . . . was it one or both, then?'

'Yes, mum,' said the client obligingly.

'What about the dog?' I tried.

The client seemed to sink into thought.

'So those involved were your grandmother, right?' I prompted. '. . . Then there was the dog? What about your brother-in-law?'

'He's an Alsatian.'

I tried subtlety. 'Um, was there one of them you *didn't* see that night?'

'I don't know what you're getting at, mum. One of what?'

'Was there someone,' I said carefully, 'whom you did not see that night?'

For a moment the weak green eyes looked blank, then his face cleared. 'I suppose you could say I didn't see me auntie,' said Mr Macaulay . . .

'Have we any witnesses?' Jim whispered to me as prosecution counsel outlined the facts for the Crown.

'It says in the instructions that the grandmother's too decrepit to give evidence and the brother-in-law's "presently unavailable", whatever that means.'

'Wormwood Scrubs, I should think. Just our luck. Oh well, we'll have to play it by ear,' remarked Jim with a sang-froid which seemed to me as magnificent as it was unaccountable. 'Would you mind taking a note by the way? Mine are never any good; can't read my own writing.'

Prosecuting counsel had meanwhile rung up the curtain on a butcher's shop in the Wandsworth area, which a police constable had been passing in the early hours of a winter morning when he noticed that it was being burgled. One of the men inside had been the defendent Macaulay. The officer testified that he had watched him scoop the contents of the till into a bag. At this stage the officer had radioed for help. After a time he had seen the defendant and his colleagues climbing up through a skylight onto the roof. Reinforcements had arrived in the shape of PCs Bean and Bowman, and the defendant and one other man had been arrested. The third had made good his escape. The officer had no doubt at all that Macaulay and the man in the shop were one and the same.

All this time Jim had been working at the pile of papers before him, trying to keep one jump ahead of the prosecution case. I wondered if Mr Macaulay had any idea of the disadvantages Jim was under, and what would have been the effect on his confidence if he had. When Jim finally rose to cross-examine, however, I was impressed even before he spoke. One needed to look no further than his ferocious expression to tell that here was a dashing and fiery advocate. Down his dark aquiline nose he glared at the police officer, who returned his glance with a look of bland innocence.

'Well, officer?' said Jim in the tone of a man with something up his sleeve.

'Sir?'

'Are we to infer that you are prepared to tell this court that beyond a peradventure . . . this man you see today in the dock is the self-same man you watched burgling that shop that night?'

'That's correct, sir.'

'You would take your Bible oath to that?'

'If you recall, I just did do, sir,' said the police officer politely.

'Hm,' said Jim in a significant tone. I guessed that this preliminary skirmish was aimed at unsettling the witness. Although so far, it had to be admitted, the policeman showed no signs of being unsettled, one could not but admire Jim's court manner.

'You told us, officer, I think, that you were standing across the road from the shop?'

'Correct, sir.'

'Let's see. How wide would the road be at that point?'

'I really didn't measure, sir.'

Jim favoured him with a look of grim assessment. Here, that look implied, was a clever Dick. 'I suppose, officer, that it might not be beyond your capabilities to make an estimate?'

'I should say a matter of some fifty feet, sir, or thereabouts.'

'Thank you. It was of course the middle of the night?'

'3.00 a.m., sir.'

'Precisely so. And this is Wandsworth; a seedy part of London – no street lighting to speak of, I suppose?'

'Not in that particular side street, sir, no.'

'Traffic still passing, I assume.'

'Well, I suppose a certain amount.'

'Officer, let's be clear: was traffic passing or was it not?'

'Well, put like that, I suppose it was, sir.'

'Very well. And you are asking this court to believe . . .' Jim's voice was a whiplash. '. . . that from some fifty feet away, at night, on the other side of the road, in the teeth of the traffic, you were able to identify my client?'

'Yes, sir.'

'You have X-ray eyes, have you?' snapped Jim.

'No, sir.'

'Then perhaps you would like to explain to the court how you managed this remarkable feat of observation?'

'The shop was lit up, sir.'

'Hm.' Jim took this setback with characteristic grit and attacked again. 'Lit up, you say, in this . . . seedy part of the town?'

I had begun to wonder if he was altogether wise in his use of the word 'seedy' to describe a part of London which was more than likely to be the home of many of the jurors.

'And in this part of London, a back street, seedy and run-down no doubt, did you not regard it as highly unusual to see a shop lit up at night?'

'Not at all, sir. In fact, that is the common practice in the area.'

'Indeed? And what might be the reason for this practice?'

'To discourage burglars because they know they can be seen, sir.'

'Hm.'

This latest blow amidships had Jim pausing for breath, but he was soon back attacking from another direction. 'Now, officer, I would be right, would I not, in saying that once you had radioed for assistance your own part in the proceedings was at an end?'

'That's correct, sir.'

'And yet you can say with certainty that this was the man you saw on the roof eighteen months before?'

'Yes, sir.'

'A man whom . . .' Jim bent his dark eyes on the jury and paused, willing them to take full note of what was coming. 'A man, I repeat, whom you had clapped eyes on for the first time that evening?'

'No, sir. Mr Macaulay and I have renewed our acquaintance on many occasions in the past five years.'

'Your honour, I object. That answer was highly prejudicial to my client.'

'Brought it on yourself, Mr Harbottle. A risky line of questioning; I thought so at the time. No good objecting now the jury have heard it. Yes? Any more questions? I daresay you'd be wise to leave it at that, Mr Harbottle, in all the circumstances.'

'Har*butt*, may it please your honour,' said Jim, driven past endurance.

'No buts about it, Mr Harbottle,' replied the judge, overruling him on this point also. 'Any re-examination, Mr Jamieson, or may this officer be dismissed?'

The case was looking unpromising for our client when a new dimension was opened up by the usher, who tapped me on the shoulder and handed me a note from the dock. It was a small and crumpled scrap of paper torn from an exercise book and on it was written the wide-ranging inquiry: *What about me brother on the roof, in court*?

I passed the note to Jim and turned to look at the public gallery. Sure enough, in the second row sat a replica of our client complete even to the corn-stook hairdo. What a piece of incredible luck. This was something which could be used to help our client, that much was obvious. The question was how.

Jim had been about to sit down when the note was handed to him. He too looked round and what he saw brought a speculative gleam to his eyes. I could almost sense his mind working round the problem even as he raised an imperious hand. 'Just a moment, officer, if you will. Are you aware the defendant has a brother?'

'I am, sir.'

'A twin brother?'

'Yes, sir.'

'Do you see the defendant's twin brother here, in this very court?'

Slowly Jim raised his arm as though aiming a pistol at the officer's chest. A pause for maximum effect, then his pointing finger began to move with the deliberation of a machine until it came to rest levelled at the pale and shifty face in the public gallery. '. . . Two peas, officer, wouldn't you say?'

'That's one way of putting it, I suppose, sir.'

'On that night, officer, that dark night, from over fifty yards away in that seedy unlit street, can you be sure that the person you say you saw in that shop was the defendant Michael Macaulay and not, for example . . . his brother?'

'Yes, sir,' said the officer comfortably. 'They look similar, I grant you, but there's no way anyone who knew them well could mistake Mick for Frank.'

'Hm. Yes, well, thank you, officer . . .'

'Besides,' went on the officer before he could be stopped. 'At the time of this offence Frank was serving a term of imprisonment. I happened to be the officer in the case. He got two years . . . for shopbreaking.'

'I already had the officer well ahead on points, but this last dreadful answer was a knockout. Poor Jim had had hardly a moment to decide what to do next when he suddenly received a buffet in the rear from a different quarter.

'Mr Harbottle, this smells strongly to me like a red herring. Are you suggesting that it was the brother who was on the roof that night; in which case, who do you say was arrested?' The judge snorted irritably. 'Is it denied that your client was there; in which case, where is his alibi notice? Stop fishing, Mr Harbottle, that's my strong advice, or you'll very shortly catch a crab.'

This hail of flak, coming on top of all his recent tribulations, seemed to find Jim Harbutt at a loss for words. Whatever crab the judge was referring to, it seemed to me that Jim with his present run of luck was bound to catch it, and I was relieved to see him dive out of harm's way into his seat.

Just as the officer was about to leave the witness-box, the usher bobbed up behind me with a second note from the dock, a grimy little twist of paper on which was written: *What about me sister in Peckham?*

I passed the thing to Jim and watched as with deliberation he tore the paper across and across into the tiniest of shreds.

'. . . And so, members of the jury, we come next to the evidence of PC Bean, who told you how he and a brother officer arrived at the scene and went in pursuit of the offenders. He said, "We put up a ladder and climbed up on the roof. On the top we found three men. I flashed . . . I'm sorry, dashed at one, causing him unfortunately to jump off the roof." And then there was evidence about calling the ambulance and putting splints on the broken leg, which you may not feel carries the case much further. He said, "I then observed this defendant Mr Macaulay hiding behind a chimneypiece. When he saw me coming, he showed alarm and attempted to jump after the first man but I managed to catch his wrists. Unfortunately because of his weight I was unable to pull him up so he dangled there until a ladder was brought." You may like to contrast this with the defendant's evidence about his pleasure and relief at seeing the officers. Questioned as to his presence on the roof at 3.30 a.m., he claimed to be walking his dog – raising the inference, I suppose, that either man or beast was a poor sleeper . . . In relation to this rooftop stroll, members of the jury, you may recall the argument advanced by defence counsel that it would be odd indeed to bring out a dog upon a criminal excursion. You will weigh that against the officer's statement in cross-examination that no dog was found. Make of it what you may; a matter for you.

'We pass now to the defendant's account of his, er, activities on that night. He said he had been "off sick" – a term of art, as it transpired, not intended to suggest that he was employed at that or any other time but merely that he was indisposed. He went, he told you, early to bed but no sooner had he "gone off" than he was awakened by a telephone call from his brother-in-law, who was apparently carrying out at that moment some urgent repairs to a leaking roof and required tools. It was then half past midnight and all the evidence was that it was a dry night. It is a matter for you whether you accept that such a telephone call was in fact made. At any rate, the defendant said he set off at once with the tools. I leave it to you to consider how useful either a jemmy or a glass-cutter might have proved in effecting repairs to a roof. The brother-in-law, we are told, was stranded on the roof although whether he in fact telephoned while in this awkward predicament must remain in the realms of speculation. The defendant told you it was then that he decided he might as well take the dog – that same dog later noted for its absence from the scene – for a walk.

'At some stage along the way, he told you, it suddenly struck him that it was his grandmother's birthday. I ought perhaps to remind you that, when asked by Mr Jamieson the date of this festival, he was unable to remember. Be that as it may, he said he decided to drop by at about 1.00 a.m., and it would appear that the plight of his brother-in-law then slipped his mind for the next hour and a half while he and the old lady sat carousing together, for he told you that it was not until about 2.30 a.m. that he and pre-sumably the phantom hound set off again in the direction of the leaking roof. He said he would have described himself as "cheerful".

'We come now to the part of the tale which may prove the greatest strain upon your credulity. As he was passing a row of shops, the defendant said, he heard strange voices calling him by name from above. What more natural therefore, he asks you to agree, than to clamber up the first drainpipe he could see? You may like to consider what you yourselves would do in like circumstances. On his arrival on the roof, the defendant said, he had the confused impression of many people running about. There were thrust into his hands what he later discovered to be a bag of cash and a stocking mask. Naturally enough, this turn of events had driven him to take refuge behind a chimneypot until the arrival of the police, when, overcome by relief, he rushed from his hiding place and tripped over, so that had the officer not seized him he would have fallen off the roof.

'Well, members of the jury, there it is. You may ask yourselves, as you are entitled to do, why neither the grandmother nor the brother-in-law has come to give evidence today: what construction should we put upon that failure? You and you alone are the judges of fact. Should you feel that I may have reached a view on any aspect of the case, discard it utterly, unless of course you agree with it. Remember the defendant has to prove nothing. Should you believe that there is or may be some shred of truth in his account, it will be your happy duty to acquit him. If, on the other hand, you reach a view that there is only one way in which any right-thinking man or woman could possibly find, then equally you must not shrink from your duty to convict. Now will you please retire and consider your verdict . . .'

'But, Jim, eighteen months' imprisonment wasn't at all bad,' I said as the taxi bucketed back across Westminster Bridge towards the Temple. 'The jury were out a full ten minutes. Considering what a record he had, I thought you did really well for him. Nobody could have done better.'

Jim looked moodily out across the parapet at a passing coal barge. 'No, the sentence was about par for the course. I can't help feeling sorry for the poor bastard, though: expecting to get Mike Deacon, whom he knows, has confidence in and so on, he lands counsel he's never clapped eyes on who knows bugger all about the case . . . Doesn't seem right somehow, does it?'

'But would it have made any difference to the result in this case? Wouldn't you have said the outcome was a foregone conclusion?'

'Well, of course it was with a court like that. Personally, I thought he was disgracefully treated in that respect. Just short of appealable, I should have said. They talk about British justice you know, but I sometimes wonder.'

'I quite agree,' I said warmly. 'I thought the summing-up was the most unfair thing I've ever heard; it was as good as a second speech for the prosecution.'

'The summing-up?' He looked surprised. 'Oh, I suppose old Lightfoot did put the boot in rather – nothing unusual. I wasn't thinking of that. It's the verdict that disgusted me.'

'The verdict?' I was astonished.

'The jury can't have been paying proper attention to my speech. There was a doubt, a definite lurking doubt, and they owed it to Macaulay to give him the benefit of it.'

'What's this?' I asked in surprise. 'I thought you made it your business to remain aloof and sceptical and never to believe your client?'

'Cobblers,' said Jim Harbutt.

7

'Now, which of you here has visited the Tower of London? Gerda, have you seen it? You have not? Marie-Claude, have you? No? Well, I really don't know.' Mr Gossage speared a last morsel of boiled mutton. 'What about you, Nils? My word, what you young foreigners *do* with yourselves is a mystery. Not to see a real historical, er, repository like the Tower is almost a crime, I should have said.' He laid down his knife and fork exactly together. 'Hasan, I believe this last turnip is going begging . . .'

I gazed up towards the street. The August evening had not yet begun to deepen into dusk. Warm light barred with shadow filtered through the railings and in at the basement kitchen window. I watched the elongated image of a black dog fleeting across the scrubbed pine surface of the long table. It reached the ketchup bottle before lifting a leg. I wished I were going out tonight on some romantic assignation – to wander entranced upon the heath with a beautiful young man and a wolfhound perhaps; to watch the evening star born from the gilded foam of sunset . . .

'. . . And therefore many were beheaded. There is one more slice left, Nils. Pass your plate if you wish to have it.'

My eyes followed the sunbeams back into the room across the wall to the door. It was panelled and brown like a chocolate bar. I wondered if there might be treacle tart and whether it would come soon. There was more to life than treacle tart, it was true, but the mutton portions had been exceptionally small.

'And in another part of the Tower you would have the opportunity of seeing air Crown Jewels: the Orb, the Sceptre and the, er . . .'

'The seat of our Shah who is in shape of a peacock is full of jewels, his back and legs also, I think,' remarked Hasan. 'He is e-foine sight. When she sit on him he shoine too much.'

Mr Gossage was just drawing breath to apply first aid to the syntax of this contribution when the door creaked open to admit Mrs Gossage, bent under the weight of a tray laden with white plates, each covered with a battered tin lid.

'Ah, there you are at last, my dear,' said Mr Gossage pleasantly, watching his wife stagger towards the sideboard. 'And what do you propose to delight us with next, if one may ask? Stack up the plates, Marie-Claude and Gerda, could you please?'

'I hope you will all enjoy our English bread pudding,' Mrs Gossage said in a piping voice, lifting one of the covers to reveal a very small and soggy brownish cube of this delicacy. 'It is a type of national dish. We in England are fond of eating it with cold custard.'

'Now, who has seen the latest exhibition at the British Museum? Charlotte, can you raise the level of our cultural understanding at all?' Mr Gossage looked as doubtful of the possibility as I felt myself.

'You know,' I said boldly, 'instead of going to exhibitions and things, visitors to this country might enjoy a visit to the courts. They would find it fascinating: the advocacy, the marvellous use of language. And of course, for those who know nothing about the law,' I added somewhat patronizingly, 'there's always the spectacle.'

'Why do you have to wear those pantomime outfits?' challenged Gareth, the Gossages' son. 'Can't you people do a day's work without dressing up first?'

'It adds to the solemnity,' I said pompously.

'If your client's likely to go to prison at the end I should think things were solemn enough in any case.'

'It's a question of carrying on tradition too; these things provide a feeling of continuity with the past.'

'So would open sewers, but that wouldn't make them particularly desirable.'

'Not at table, dear,' said his mother automatically.

'Well, anyway, what I mean to say is that in my opinion the English system of justice is the best in the world,' I said, ignoring the fact that I was ignorant of any other system. 'And I'm ready to say I'd be proud to show it off to anyone.'

I hewed off a piece of bread pudding and put it firmly into my mouth, where it bulged indestructibly like a cork in the neck of a jar.

'It's interesting that you should say that at just this moment, Charlotte,' effervesced Mrs Gossage. 'How unaccountable are the ways of providence, don't you think?'

'Absolutely,' I agreed with my mouth full, wondering uneasily what providence had up its sleeve.

'I received a letter the other day from a very old friend, an American lady from Florida, who is making a one-day visit to London as part of a tour of Europe. Quite remarkable at her age – well, what must she be? Getting on for eighty now, I suppose. Anyway she's, as the Americans would put it, a real old bundle of fun. She writes that she would like to arrange a get-together.'

'Well, that does sound exciting.'

'Yes, doesn't it? Unfortunately though, as so often happens, her visit coincides with the date our daughter is due to go in to have her feet done. Such a shame. It did just happen to strike me that the ideal solution might be if you could do me the favour of taking Mrs Crockford under your wing for the day and show her the Inns of Court and so on.'

'Are you sure Mrs Crockford would be interested?' I asked dubiously, thinking how very far from ideal this plan seemed from any point of view except Mrs Gossage's own. I had never expected my ill-considered offer to come home to roost so fast.

'Oh yes, that's the sort of thing all Americans enjoy – old crimes and history and so on,' said Mrs Gossage. 'Of course, if you're too busy, dear, and the worst comes to the worst, I can always ask Gareth to drop her in at the waxworks, but it wouldn't be quite the same.'

'No, I don't suppose it would. Well, naturally, I'll be happy to,' I said, plagued by a vision of poor Mrs Crockford gathering dust in a corner at Madame Tussaud's.

'You will? Oh, how kind.' Mrs Gossage pulled out the lace handkerchief tucked at her waist and signalled the end of dinner with an unusually cheery wave like a railway guard on the Holiday Express.

The day of Mrs Crockford's visit dawned less than a week later, fine and hot. I spent a long morning in chambers drafting an advice on the subject of a decease partially intestate.

'. . . Not a partial decease intestate, as you have it here, young Hunter. We are informed that partial decease is impossible, although looking around me I sometimes take leave to doubt it. Oh, that puts me in mind of the affidavit you did in Harness . . . Hornett . . . What was the name of that case? Ah, here we are, Hooley.' Freddy produced two or three handwritten sheets from a drawer and slid them across the desk. 'Better, dear girl. You seem to have covered most of the main points. I note, by the way, that you've taken to heart my advice about using an affidavit to appeal to the reader's emotions, but do bear in mind on whose behalf . . . Yes, you see here, for example: "This event caused me untold distress." From a wife whose husband's run off, perfectly suitable. Not so good from a farmer talking about late delivery of a tractor engine. These are small stylistic points which will come with practice. You'll see I've made one or two minor amendments.' I turned over pages covered with such a riot of crossings-out and substitutions in blue pencil that the original was unreadable. 'Nil desperandum, dear girl.' Freddy grinned at the sight of my face. 'If you knew it all, you wouldn't be here would you? Besides,' he added, 'I found your little date chart very helpful. Ah, talking of that, isn't today the day you're meeting your old party? Off you go then. Could you be a good girl and drop these off in the clerks' room for typing on your way out?'

I took the thin set of papers with reverent hands. 'For typing? You don't mean to say these are . . . finished?'

'A certain degree of urgency, Percival informs me. I'm against the principle of allowing solicitors to feel they can start swooping down on papers and taking them back whenever the fancy moves them, although in fairness I suppose eleven months . . . Oh, by the way, should you happen to see Percival in the clerks' room perhaps you'd give him a message: we found the Chateau Margaux he produced very palatable and I've got the Latour '61 for him to try, but it might be the better of a little more keeping.' He paused. 'I don't know though. On second thoughts, don't tell him anything of the sort. Ask him to step in here for a moment when he's free. I've decided to sample it.'

The clerks' room was as usual the scene of much activity. Paul at his table behind the door was typing fee-notes hunt and peck with one finger, Kathy at her huge machine by the window was hammering away like a sten gun at the backlog of paperwork and Norman was on the telephone. In the middle of the room Jim Harbutt and the walrus were having a discussion about fees, of the kind often described by spokesmen as a free and frank exchange of views.

'Yes but, damn it, Percival, leaving aside the question of five guineas for the advice, three for the statement of claim is paltry, absolute peanuts. I mean, just think about it . . .'

Percival appeared to think about it. 'Well, sir, I'll charge five for that and three for the advice, if you prefer,' he said equably. 'All the same to me.'

'Yes, and to me too: eight miserable guineas,' said Jim bitterly. 'Peanuts, Percival. Added to which, by the time I get paid in two or more years' time, the value of the pound may have halved for all we know. It's shocking.'

'It's the going rate for the job, sir.'

'Do you realize how much that represents in terms of payment per hour?' demanded Jim. 'If you consider that those two pleadings must have taken, let's see . . . reading the papers, looking up the law, finding a number of authorities, writing . . . I don't know – say, sixteen hours of my time as a qualified professional man. For how much? Less than ten bob an hour. It's just not good enough, with all due respect, Percival.'

'You'll just have to speed up, sir,' said the walrus, shifting to the attack. 'If you'll forgive me for saying so, you can't afford to get yourself a name for being slow at your papers. It won't do, sir. Seven days in and out, that should be the rule. Speedy and deedy, that's what I tell all the young men; Miss Hunter here, for example, will remember me saying that only the other day.'

'Well, peculiar as it may seem, I came to the Bar in the hope of making a living,' said Jim stormily. 'Look at my uncle at the tax Bar. I happen to know he charges in excess of ten pounds a page for an advice. Puts out a thirty-page advice as a matter of course. Makes a mint, by all accounts.'

'Well, for that matter, we could charge by weight and give savings stamps away with each half-pound affidavit,' said the walrus with a loud bark of laughter at his own joke. 'No, but seriously, sir, how your uncle may choose to feather his own . . . I should say, structure his own scale of fees is none of my concern. The fees I charge for you, sir, are another matter. As long as I'm your clerk, you can rely on me to get you the proper fee, and eight guineas, sir, is the rate for this job.' Percival brought up a flipper and smacked it against the side of

Paul's desk in a decisive manner. Paul jumped, swore and reached for the Tipp-Ex bottle.

'I'd be prepared to compromise at eighteen guineas for the two,' continued Jim hopefully.

'You really are a most mercenary young man, Mr Harbutt,' Percival remarked with a sentential shake of his jowls. 'What are you, three years called? You know, in my young days a man of twenty years' call would have travelled as far as Carlisle with his brief marked at no more than five and two, just for the sake of exposure in court and thought nothing of it.'

'Well, I don't think much of it, either. And as for exposure . . .' Jim lifted one foot to show a worn patch on the sole of his shoe through which a small area of puce sock could be seen. 'I should be glad to be able to afford a new pair before winter comes round again.'

'Percival, Gordon's on. Matter of fixing a fee in *Saltraker* v. *Barmouth UDC*. Will you have a word?'

Percival folded a fin round the receiver Norman handed up and breathed avuncularly into it. As he listened, presumably to some figure being proposed, his liquid eyes became hooded and dim. Periodically he shook his heavy head so that the dewlaps beneath swung dolefully from side to side.

'Hold it, Gordon, hold it,' he said at last in the desolate tone of a northern lightship. 'I'll be honest with you, Gordon . . . Yes, that's right . . . Well quite . . . And so would my job be if I were to let Mr Ap William go into court for less than . . . Well, I'd have to say a couple of thousand on the brief . . . The very best I could do, with three hundred a day refreshers. Anything less would be laughable.' He gave a gusty wheeze full of unspeakable sorrow. 'You're squeezing me, Gordon, squeezing me. He couldn't open the papers for under two thousand; couldn't look at them . . . Right, right, Gordon, you go back to the local authority by all means. Mark you,' he sighed miserably, 'it wouldn't surprise me if we were to be hearing from Saltraker's within the day. Well, it comes to this, say to them: which side is prepared to pay for the best. Simple as that. Be hearing . . . Hff.'

Noblesse apparently not obliging him as head clerk to go through the niceties needed to end the conversation, Percival removed the receiver from his ear and held it dangling in the air until Norman retrieved it and said what was necessary.

'Think they'll be back?' Norman asked.

'I don't foresee any bother,' said the walrus. 'They'll come to the boil in their own good time. And now, Mr Harbutt, were there any other points? No? I should get those shoes mended if I were you. Can't afford to go round looking poor, you know. Wrong image for a barrister.' He brushed a speck of dust from his premier-quality-worsted bosom. 'And if you'll take my advice, sir, you'll shed the pink socks. Don't want to be taken for a lefty at any price. Well, I shall be on my way unless . . Ah, Miss Hunter, was there something?'

I gave the message about the wine. 'Oh, and I brought this for typing,' I said, producing Freddy's bit of work.

'What's this, a piece of work? Finished, d'you say? Good show. Here, Norman, d'you see this? Mr Tobin's turned out a bit of work. Well, well.'

'*Manley* v. *Manley*? Thank Christ. Fraser's are coming for that this afternoon. Kicked up no end of stink.'

Norman flipped the papers onto the top of the backlog piled on Kathy's desk. 'Give us a bit of priority on those could you, Kath. Good girl.' Wearily he pulled open a desk drawer, brought out a sandwich and began absentmindedly to eat it while hunting for some entry in the diary. Two telephones began to ring.

'Well, I shall go now, I believe,' said the walrus, moving his grey bulk down the passage in the direction of Freddy's room and the Chateau Latour. I went down the stairs and out into the sunshine.

After the cavernous coolness of the hallway the air outside was hot, with a summery tang of asphalt and dry grass. As I made my way up through Pump Court towards my rendezvous with Mrs Crockford outside the law courts, I found myself increasingly nervous. The whole expedition seemed ill judged. Why should this poor old lady who had come so far to look up a few of her closest friends want to spend the afternoon trailing round the law courts with someone she had never clapped eyes on? And even if for some unfathomable reason she should want to do so, what if it proved too much? The journey between any two points inside the law courts was arduous and long; suppose she made it halfway up the stairs and then stuck or had a fainting attack? Suppose she collapsed and fell down the steps?

It did not bear thinking of. Instead, I conjured up thoughts about Mrs Gossage and what I might have liked to do to her with a barrel of boiling oil and a set of spikes at my disposal.

I reached the great doorway of the law courts and looked up at the clock. Five minutes to go. So far there was no sign of the old woman. I suddenly found myself trying quite hard to remember the basic lifesaving drill I had learned for a bronze swimming medal at school.

Idly I watched the passers-by on their way to lunch: barristers crossing the road from the courts with purposeful tread; watchful-looking men in soft hats headed for the Clachan bar. Flocks of young girls in strappy dresses and evening sandals twittered here and there, colourful and lightheaded as sunbirds. A woman leading a white miniature poodle stopped in front of me to allow it to foul the pavement, and was collided with hard from behind by a young man reading a book. The dog, an old one, regarded the assailant narrowly from rust-shadowed eyes. The woman burst into a volley of barks.

'Serve you right,' commented an old lady in a black bonnet. 'Letting that beast leave its droppings.' She pointed her stick at the offender standing rather sheepishly beside a small pile of turds. 'What about the kiddies?' demanded the crone. 'Poor mites can't play safely anywhere these days.'

'Come on, mother,' said a male voice from somewhere.

'You watch who you're calling mother, cheeky bastard.' said the old woman shrilly. 'Ought to be destroyed you did,' she added, either to the poodle or its owner, before the dammed-up wave of pedestrians broke over the tableau and washed the young man, both women and the dog away down the street.

Meanwhile a number of taxis had drawn up, bringing in succession a stout young couple in glasses, two older men, an elegant woman in a green suit and one or two others I failed to notice. No sign of Mrs Crockford. I was just beginning to think with some relief that she must have decided not to come, when another taxi arrived. Out of it slowly climbed an extremely old woman in a black bombazine outfit draped with an assortment of dark rugs and shawls and carrying rather surprisingly a Gladstone bag which she put down on the pavement while fishing in her purse for the fare. Politely I approached, smiling a welcome. Black beady eyes regarded me warily from a face of yellow crumpled parchment.

'Well, good afternoon, Mrs Crockford,' I said picking up the Gladstone bag. 'How very nice to meet you.'

Noticing that she had not responded to my greeting save to withdraw like a tarantula towards the edge of the pavement, I added in a loud voice in case she should be deaf, 'I'm Charlotte Hunter, you know; there's no need to worry.'

Suddenly the old woman shot out an arm and pointed past me at the law court building. 'Harrots,' she cracked out in a thick accent. 'I am for Harrots sale.' And, snatching back the Gladstone bag, she toiled up the steps and disappeared into the courts.

I was staring bemusedly after her when a voice behind me said, 'Excuse me, did I hear you ask for Mrs Crockford?'

I turned to find myself confronted by the elegant woman in the green suit.

'I'm Marian Crockford.' I had the impression that she was trying not to laugh. She must have been in her fifties, but remarkably well kept: willowy, with ash-blond hair which accentuated the deep bronze of her skin. She wore a good deal of gold jewellery and a huge green stone flashed on one lacquer-tipped finger. It seemed astonishing that this sophisticated woman should be a friend of Mrs Gossage, and yet here she was, smiling, enveloping me in a haze of French perfume, holding out little hands with the fine-boned strength of birds to clasp my arm – all with a bubbling stream of small friendly exclamations: 'Just you go right ahead now and call me Marian. And you're Caroline Hunter, am I right? You won't mind my calling you Caroline, I hope? Oh . . . Charlotte? Why, what a lovely name. You've no idea, Charlotte, how perfectly delighted I am to make your acquaintance and I want you to know that I take it as a real kindness on your part to have come so far and given up your day for my sake.'

From the way she spoke, it might have been I, not she, who had come three thousand miles across the Atlantic.

'Myra Gossage called me last evening,' she said as we set off, 'and told me you were the very person to tell me all there is to know about the English legal system. I just can hardly wait.' She turned a pair of piercingly blue eyes upon me as though expecting a quick dissertation on the spot. At close quarters I could see she was older than I had thought; the skin which stretched taut across the fine facial bones had none of the elasticity of youth and her neck was filigreed with tiny lines. Yet those eyes had the clear, penetrating gaze which is seldom seen in a person older than twelve. As we passed through the upper Temple gateway, she said, as though reading my thoughts, 'I guess you were expecting to meet a really old lady?'

'I misunderstood Mrs Gossage. You'll never believe this, but I thought she said you were eighty years old.'

Marian Crockford laughed delightedly. 'Eighty? Lord's sake, what can Myra Gossage have been thinking of? Why, I'm not even seventy-six until October. Well now, my dear, I'm ready to get started right this minute. I want to know everything about everything . . .'

This was no exaggeration, but a literal statement of fact. I had never met anyone in my life who asked so many questions. Was this called Pomp Court as in *Pomp and Circumstance*, she wanted to know. Oh, Pump Court? Well, had there once been a pump here? What had become of it? The Cloisters? Did that mean there had been an abbey here? Had monks lived in the Temple? The Wars of the Roses had really started in this rose garden here? What date would that have been? What were the dates of the Crusades? How had lawyers first come here? How many Temples of Court were there? Was there a ladies' powder room?

Having replied to the last of this barrage of inquiries – the only one I could answer with entire confidence – I sat down on the library steps in the sunshine and closed my eyes. This afternoon I would buy Marian a tourists' guide. In the meantime what was needed was the fortification of a good meal.

'I thought you might like to lunch in the Middle Temple Hall,' I said to my guest casually on her return. 'An interesting new experience, you know . . .'

It was a bullseye. Marian's eyes grew round as sapphire saucers in anticipation of the treat.

The interior of the hall looked resplendent. Sunlight gleamed upon the dark patina of old wood and deepened the heraldic colours of the crested panels. Proudly I pointed towards the roof, assuring my guest that this was said to be the second-finest double-hammer-beamed ceiling in England. 'Indeed, in the world, I shouldn't wonder,' I added, carried away by enthusiasm. Marian gazed raptly upwards. Was that really so? Could I explain how hammer beams were fixed up there and what wood they were made from; whether the hammers were for some purpose, and if so what? What year did the roof date from? Where was the finest ceiling if this was the second finest, and in what way was that finer than this?

'Here,' I said. 'I bet you haven't noticed this frieze. Do you know that during the war a bomb came in and blew it to bits, but one of the Masters of the Bench had some workmen collect the pieces in sacks so that afterwards it could be reconstructed exactly as you see it now. Amazing, isn't it?'

Amazing, Marian agreed, regarding the carved tracery with delighted appreciation. What exactly was the carving supposed to depict? Who had the carver been and what kind of wood was it? Was it too dark for oak, did I think; oriental hardwood perhaps? When would it date from exactly? Had there been a first Master of the Bench, founding father, and if so who and when?

'Here, let me show you the crests on this wall,' I said, steering her off in another direction. 'Then after that I expect you'd like something to eat.'

'You know, Charlotte dear,' Marian said as we stood before a large portrait the name of whose subject had temporarily slipped my mind. 'I just can never tell you how I have enjoyed seeing this wonderful place. There is a quality . . .' She spread her arms wide. 'It's hard to describe, but somehow to me these lovely and historic things you've been showing me seem to . . . speak for themselves.'

In the light of my abilities as a guide, this struck me as fortunate.

Lunch was by now in full swing and the hall was crowded with barristers sitting at the long refectory tables bellowing at each other above the institutional clatter of knives and forks. Far from the dignified rituals of dinner, lunch was a scene of constant motion. White-coated stewards moved back and forth with plates and trays. Those coming in to eat percolated up the aisles looking for places on the wooden benches, so that those already eating were continually having to shuffle along to make room or duck as newcomers climbed over the table to fill spaces against the wall. Those who had finished could be seen hopping about trying to bring their legs out from beneath the table without dislodging their neighbours – a procedure which, I had been told, could roll a whole benchload of people backwards onto the floor, although regretfully I had not so far seen this happen. A long queue at the old-fashioned paydesk blocked one of the aisles and caused additional confusion as incomers and stewards pushed past this living centipede and trod on its feet.

'Well now, come along then,' I said to my guest in a hospitable way, indicating a small gap between two barristers on a bench. 'Do sit down and make yourself comfortable.' No sooner had I said it than I realized I was asking the impossible. Given the tightness and straightness of her skirt, the height of her heels, and the fact that the distance between the two barristers could have been no more than thirty inches, there was no way in which she could have got onto that bench without rucking up her skirt around her waist. From the look on her face I could see that this prospect had also occurred to Marian. In the end, three barristers rose from the bench and stood courteously watching as she swung her legs up and across it, laddering a stocking in the process. Dreadfully embarrassed, I apologized. The problem had not struck me before, I said. No, no, replied my redoubtable guest; it had been an interesting new experience, besides throwing a sidelight upon the position of women in the legal profession over here.

Marian's neighbour split open a bread roll and began telling someone on the other side of the table in some detail about his client's wife, who had been dredged from the River Colne – rather a long time after the event, it seemed – and how the pathological experts had set about trying to discover the identity of the corpse and the cause of death, which might have been due to some form of poisoning. I decided on sausages and mash. Bloating had made any assessment of the time of death more difficult. What would Marian like to eat, I asked. Looking on the pale side, she wondered if there was something lighter available as it was still only breakfast-time in Florida.

The steward assigned to our table was, I remembered with dismay, a temperamental man who, if he took a dislike to any of his clients, would ignore them for as long as possible and then arrive with tripe and onions. I realized that we must be on his blacklist ten minutes later when he served our neighbours with bowls of steaming wallpaper paste and rushed off before I could catch him. What was I to do? After the upheaval involved in getting Marian onto this bench I could scarcely ask her to move to another. On the other hand, tripe and onions? Still with one eye on the vagrant steward, I picked up one of the luncheon slips from the table and began filling in our order.

Fortunately Marian did not seem bored, having struck up a conversation with her neighbour on the other side, a man in his early fifties, I judged, with a nondescript face and a pompous air. The steward arrived with a plate of sausages for him and went away, ignoring my frantic semaphore. I felt my face grow pink with irritation.

'I should have thought,' he was remarking in a disapproving tone, 'that any woman nowadays who makes it clear that she regards herself as standing on an equal footing with men is very liable to be treated accordingly – though why a woman should choose to throw away her natural advantages I personally cannot imagine. *Vive la différence* is what I say every time.'

'Oh, and how right you are,' cried Marian warmly if somewhat vaguely. 'Charlotte, are you and this gentleman acquainted? He has just been telling me some of his very fascinating beliefs about the position of men and women in the legal profession.'

'Yes, so I heard,' I said.

'I think it's just marvellous,' said Marian with a feminine little laugh, 'to see clever young things like Charlotte here competing to become attorneys and being called to this wonderful Temple and all. I just never could have . . . aspired' – she lowered her lashes demurely – 'to hold myself up on an equal footing with . . . a man.'

'I won't attempt to conceal,' said her neighbour judicially, 'that in my view women are neither physically nor emotionally equipped for life at the Bar; not mentally equipped for it either. And they're not particularly good speakers,' he added for good measure. 'Speaking for myself, I'd say they were a disruptive influence in chambers too. All they succeed in doing is losing their femininity, which is objectionable enough in itself but, if you take that sort of thing to its logical conclusion, what do you get? Well, take these women's liberators, or whatever they call themselves: a whole lot of lesbies running around doing no good to man or beast.'

He put a large chunk of sausage into his mouth and chewed it in a masterful manner. I flexed my muscles resentfully beneath the Bulgarian suit. Although a great believer in feminine helplessness myself, particularly where motor cars or mortgages are concerned, it has always galled me to have womanliness held up as a sort of moral duty.

'Why do you talk about "lesbies" like that?' I asked. 'Sexual proclivities have nothing to do with wanting a better deal. You wouldn't call men in a picket line "a whole lot of poofters", would you?'

'I should have thought the difference was too obvious to need any explanation.'

'Well, if by "losing one's femininity" you mean not wanting to be second rate, I should think the sooner it's lost the better.' I was finding this man quite abominable.

He gave a chauvinistic shrug. 'Another thing about women is that they are incapable of debating a point without getting emotional. An absolutely basic disadvantage at the Bar.'

'Well, all I can say is, it's lucky your views are no longer held by anybody with sense,' I said, choosing a moment when he had piled in a forkful of cabbage and was unable to reply. 'Not meaning to sound rude, I've never heard such a lot of Victorian . . . cobblers.' I stopped, fearing that I had gone too far and that he might seize the advantage with a peroration about the unsuitability of foul-mouthed women for legal life.

'My dear girl,' he said with insufferable patronage when he could eventually speak. 'If there should ever come a day when you have been at the Bar for as long as I have, you may well find you have learned enough to share my views.' He turned to Marian, dismissing me. 'In the meantime, dear lady, I notice you have nothing to eat. Aren't you being looked after?'

'I believe there may have been a little trouble in calling the attention of that man in white . . .' Marian's voice tailed off rather helplessly. 'But please don't let us bother you. A person like yourself must have many more important things on his mind, and I'm sure that sooner or later Charlotte will manage . . .'

'Nonsense. We can't allow a charming lady guest to be kept waiting.'

So saying, he glanced towards the steward and made an almost imperceptible motion of the head. The waiter put down his tray and came rushing up. 'Sir?'

'I believe these ladies are waiting to order,' said our champion with manly firmness. 'And now I must ask you to excuse me.'

Marian smiled her thanks. The steward and I looked sourly at one another. Slowly he picked up the luncheon form from the table and read what I had absentmindedly written. 'Two orders of tripe and onions?'

Just for a split second his face revealed surprise. Then with a vinegary smile of satisfaction he shook his head. 'Too late. Tripe and onion's finished.'

So there was a silver lining after all.

8

'Why, doesn't it look just like sugar candy?'

Marian craned her neck to gaze upward at the pinnacled white outline of the law courts across the road. 'It's pure fairytale, dear. I feel I could just run right over there and snap off one of those spires like a lollipop.'

'You can't do that, it's only just been cleaned,' I said. 'I've got an intellectual feast for you instead. By the greatest piece of luck your visit has happened to coincide with a very important libel action against a society magazine.'

I had been given this information earlier in the day by Norman. ('There should be quite a few film stars in court. If the lady's from Florida that should make her feel at home,' he had said with a fine disregard for geographical matters. 'Besides, Dodgwick's appearing for the paper.' What were a few hundred film stars more or less, his tone implied, if Dodgwick QC were appearing? I tried to look at it from this professional viewpoint but it was hard work.)

'There should be people from the film world there,' I said.

'Oh, Charlotte, that should be truly thrilling.'

'And that's not all. Dodgwick is appearing.'

'Why, just imagine that,' breathed Marian, rising to the occasion. 'How perfectly delightful. And how dear of you, Charlotte, to think of showing me the dodgwick too. I simple cannot wait to see it.'

'Er, "him" actually, Marian,' I said, thinking momentarily of Hasan. 'Gerald Dodgwick is the most famous defamation silk in the Temple.' I had got this information from Graham Webster, not having liked to admit my ignorance to Norman.

'Charlotte dear, the most famous defamation . . . what?'

'The senior barristers, Queen's Counsel, are called "silks" because they wear silk gowns,' I said informatively. 'Junior barristers, you see, wear gowns made of something different called "stuff".'

'Ah, don't tell me . . . you junior people are called "stuffs"?'

'Well no, although I can think of some who ought to be – like that ghastly prehistoric character at lunch, for example. Look, here we are in what we call the Great Hall. It was built in Victorian times. The Bar Clerks' Association play badminton here on Wednesday evenings.'

She clasped her hands together and gazed round delightedly, admiring the sweep of the mosaic floor, the cloistered galleries and the great dark interior of the roof.

'Why, how perfectly breathtaking.' She took hold of my arm. 'Charlotte, you simply must tell me all you know about this place . . .'

Since I already had, I thought it best not to linger but speeded her towards the main spiral staircase leading up to the gallery.

'Where now? I can hardly wait to see this Dodgwick of yours in his silk dress.'

'Gown,' I said. 'Quite a different thing altogether. This way.'

The afternoon proceedings were just about to begin. Three leading counsel, each with a junior behind him, were already in the silks' row near the front, surrounded by the residue of a hard morning's work. Documents and leather-jacketed volumes lay all about. The bench was a white wasteland of paper in which the sole reminder of human occupation was a small pair of spectacles clinging crablike to the wreckage. The courtroom was in the style of the last century, lined with seasoned wood-panelling and smelling of leather bindings and polish. The clerk of the court, who by the look of him might also have been a Victorian relic, sat wigged and gowned at the foot of a great timber cliff upon the crest of which perched the bench – so precipitous a vantage point was it that much of what happened at the front of the court would be invisible to the judge, and presumably also inaudible. I suppose that the designer had decided that such small practical sacrifices were worthwhile in the pursuit of splendour.

'Well, what do you think?' I inquired rather prematurely in the loud church whisper which seems to come naturally in large public places.

'Magnificent. Truly magnificent,' church-whispered my guest politely. 'Where's the dock?'

'There isn't one. This is a civil court.'

'Oh, I see.' She sounded disappointed, so I pointed out the

witness-box, into which the black-gowned usher was just then helping a fat old gentleman in a skull-cap and prayer vest. Had I perhaps seen his picture in the papers? He had the look of a film director, I thought excitedly, apart perhaps from the prayer vest. As I had not up to then done much to increase my guest's understanding of the English legal system, past or present, I would have been very pleased to gain lost ground by suavely identifying the fat old man. But I had no idea who he was. Dare I hope that just this once Marian might forget to ask?

'Who's that old person in the box there?' whispered Marian dead on cue. 'Is he well known?'

'World-famous film director,' I hissed back. 'Er, are you comfortable?'

This was a fatuous inquiry since already the hardness of the bench was becoming noticeable, but at least it changed the subject.

'Tell me now, which is Dodgwick?'

'I'm afraid it's a bit hard to tell from behind.'

I did not add that it would have been equally difficult from the front as I had never seen this paragon before, any more than I had seen the old man in the skull-cap. I was beginning to wish the proceedings would start and put an end to Marian's investigations. It was a pity too that the film stars had not yet come back from lunch; at present, the public benches were only sparsely filled. To have had some famous faces here would certainly have added to the excitement. On the other hand, it might have made matters worse – I probably would not have recognized them either.

Fortunately at that moment the action began. The usher drew himself up and shouted in a parade-ground bellow, 'Goortrai!'

'What does that mean?' hissed Marian, startled.

'It means get up,' I explained. 'The judge is coming in.'

The judge, in dark civil robes, appeared through a velvet-draped doorway on the bench and seated himself upon the great throne beneath a coat of arms in red and gold. One of the three leaders was on his feet. A very tall, tawny-haired man of impressive presence, he made me think of some awesome bird of prey: an eagle on a rocky crag perhaps. Yes, I thought with pleasure, this man was, as Hasan would say, e-foine sight.

Marian nudged me. 'Who's that? My, he's so glamorous. Is it Dodgwick?'

I felt a twinge of irritation. Children and tourists never knew when they were lucky. Take a child to the zoo and show it the last known captive panda and it will ask if there are any guinea pigs. Now here I was offering Marian a sight of sheer barristerial perfection and what did she want? Dodgwick. I had begun to think I had made a bad mistake in mentioning Dodgwick.

Marian touched my arm. 'Is it?'

I slowly raised one hand and put on a heavy expression as though I expected the eagle to lead us in prayer. I hoped he would say something before she had a chance to ask me anything else.

'M'please yer lardsheep,' said the eagle, suddenly to my great relief taking flight. 'Might I before we resume seek yer lardsheep's leave to interpose in relation to those of me larned friend's submissions which directly preceded the luncheon adjournment in point of time a swift rebuttal albeit not I hasten to say of that which went to the meat and heart of such submission yet nonetheless germane in substance . . .'

My relief at his having found voice had given way to dismay on hearing the voice he had found: reedy and peppered with strange affectations. His splendid appearance had been too good to be true, it seemed.

'. . . Nay, me lud, I know not. I should doubtless hasten to clarify the position thus: I know not but that were yer lardsheep minded to take a certain course I would rest my submission without more, save to say that there may come a time in the fullness of, er . . . time, when a further application may prove apposite. Alternatively were yer lardsheep minded at this stage to accede to any part of me larned friend's submission I should be obliged to address yer lardsheep further. Might I say, I should hope to be short.'

'What's he saying, dear?' asked Marian under her breath.

'He says: if the judge agrees with his opponent he'll make a long speech,' I translated.

'That's blackmail,' said Marian decisively.

The judge said something inaudible.

'As yer ludsheep pleases,' said the eagle and sank like a deflated silk balloon.

Up rose the second silk to cross-examine. Although he lacked the fine presence of the eagle, being small, red-faced and rather plump, his court manner was important to say the least. Drawing himself up until he stood on tiptoe he slowly donned his spectacles, moved them to the end of his nose and peered disdainfully at the witness. He then rocked back onto his heels, whipped the glasses off and used them as a lorgnette to stare in the manner of a stage duchess at the old man in the prayer vest who peered back with mild interest over the high side of the witness-box. Finally the silk cast his spectacles away onto the pile of papers before him, hooked his thumbs into his gown fronts in true theatrical style, cleared his throat and said in a deep and resonant voice, 'Er, bombly beeb mm bbly; bombly beeb dbly?'

'I beg your pardon?' said the witness.

The inquisitor spoke more resoundingly still. 'Bombly beeb mm bbly; bombly beeb dbly?'

Marian put a reluctant hand on my arm. 'I'm just so sorry for all these interruptions. Could you tell me what this one's saying? Lord's sakes, I must be going deaf.'

'Could you re-phrase that question perhaps?' suggested the witness.

The questioner pondered for a moment. 'Goob goob, wob ha wob na?'

'I think he's got some kind of speech impediment; there's something not right about his consonants,' I said doubtfully.

'The poor man,' said Marian, looking unconvinced; and indeed so confident did the speaker appear to be that it was hard to believe there was anything amiss. I could tell that my guest believed he was speaking some antique language of the courts.

'Harble boob, hamble bon,' he continued.

This brought counsel for the plaintiff to his feet. It struck me at once that this smooth-faced man bore more than a passing resemblance to one of those small dinosaurs with little praying hands and a reputation for running up and biting others from behind. For a moment he regarded his opponent with the in curious stony gaze of a lizard, then suddenly opened his mouth with a snap and hissed at the judge. The other leader subsided billowing onto the bench. I leaned forward, my ears combing the hushed air of the courtroom to catch what dim sibilants I could.

'Ts . . . ps.'

At this up shot the small silk. 'Bobble na, er, booble na . . .'

'Ss . . . ds.'

'Did you catch that, Charlotte?'

'Dobble, dobble . . .'

I had no idea what the argument was about but it was clear that opinion was deeply divided. The small silk was redder in the face than ever and it seemed that the dinosaur was more than a little steamed under the plates. I felt myself growing warm with secret embarrassment as I remembered all I had said to Marian earlier about the standard of advocacy in these courts. Although I was not as discriminating as I would have liked to think and sometimes had trouble distinguishing a good speech from a soufflé of hot air, even I could tell that between them these three combined just about every cardinal fault available to a public speaker.

Battle had now reached its height, with such a crossfire of hissing and bobbling that the judge decided that it was time to intervene. Raising an authoritative hand, he prepared to pour oil upon the waters of conflict. For what seemed an age the court lay hushed and expectant awaiting some pronouncement from the bench, while the judge sat wordlocked, grappling with a stammer so severe that it was a full minute at least before he could make a sound.

'What is it, dear?' whispered Marian. 'Did somebody say something funny?'

A short time after this the eagle's junior, a man of fairly advanced years, apparently made up his mind that the excitement was over for the day. Slowly and with deliberation, he folded his arms in front of him on the desk, pulled his wig down over his face and peacefully withdrew from the proceedings.

'Why, Charlotte, I can hardly believe my eyes. What on earth is that man doing?'

'Just knocking off for a few minutes; taking a bit of a rest, you know,' I said, secretly rather astonished myself by this blatant lack of pretence.

'But isn't it against the rules? Do they have watches, like in the navy?'

'Actually, he may look relaxed but he's really quite alert, taking it all in. It's a matter of training. You'll be surprised – a hint of anything untoward and he'll be up like a shot.'

The relaxing man let out a rich snore. A colleague elbowed him covertly in the ribs. I had to admit that in considering the cardinal faults of public speakers I had not thought to include unconsciousness . . .

Outside in the corridor poor Marian looked at me in an expectant manner, wondering what I had in store for her next.

'Of course, that sort of thing is all very well and good in its way,' I said – failing to define in what way anything we had seen could possibly be described as well or good. 'It seemed to me, though, that as a lay person you might prefer to watch something a bit . . . livelier. Here, let's try this.' I guided her towards the court next door, comforting myself with the thought that whatever might be going on in there it could hardly fail to be livelier than what we had left.

The second court looked almost exactly like the first, apart from an empty silks' row which told me that Dodgwick had eluded us once again. This appeared to be a defended divorce. In the witness-box stood a grey-haired woman in a striped cotton dress like a well-plumped pillowcase from which capable arms extended.

'Now, Mrs Basnet, thinking back to that Tuesday, did there come a time when you met the respondent?'

'Yes, there did.'

'Where did this meeting take place?'

'Well, I was standing in the lounge, you know, hoovering.'

'And the respondent, where was he standing?'

'Well, he wasn't – that's to say, not standing.'

'What was he doing?'

'I suppose you'd say hanging there, really.'

'Hanging where, madam?'

'From a beam in the sitting room.'

'Do you mean tied up?'

'Well no, sort of gripping on, I'd say. Straphanging like in the tube trains.'

'Was he dressed normally?'

'I shouldn't say so exactly, sir, no.'

'What was he wearing, to the best of your recollection?'

'Well let me see: fishnet tights, a corset. There was a dog's collar, you know, with studs round his neck, I seem to remember . . . sandals.'

'Did he say anything to you?'

'He said, "I'm a Roman slave girl, Mrs Basnet." I said, "So I see, sir" – to humour him, you know.'

'Did he say anything else?'

'Yes, he asked me to smack him with my broom handle.'

'And did you, er, oblige?'

'I said, "Sir, I'm sorry but I've work to be getting on with."'

'Were there any further incidents of this kind?'

'Only one that I can remember, when he jumped me in the broom cupboard. I opened it to get the hoover and he jumped out. Gave me quite a turn.'

'Did he appear normal?'

'I don't know about him but I wasn't feeling too well after that, speaking for meself.'

'I think that in the November you left the parties' employ of your own accord?'

'Yes, sir.'

'Could you tell us the reason for your leaving?'

'I didn't like the way they treated their animals, sir.'

The respondent was next into the witness-box and was cross-examined in detail about something he kept referring to as 'malarky'. There had been a good deal of this, and I was becoming uneasily aware that nothing we were hearing about it was suitable for the ears of a respectable seventy-five-year-old lady. I ought to take her away but the thought of moving her again was more than I could bear.

'Now, Mr P., whose idea was the knotted rope?'

'The rope was only an experiment; we normally used leather thongs.'

While I sat hoping that the standard of decency would improve, it began to seem that attention had focused on every item of rubber equipment known to frogmen apart from an actual diving-bell, and enough leather to stock a saddler's shop. At one stage there was even mention of a policeman's helmet, although where it had come from and what use was made of it I did not grasp. Marian had fallen silent. I was too mortified to look in her direction and so could only guess what was going through her mind, but my thoughts were most uncomfortable. The fact that the standard of advocacy was noticeably higher did nothing to raise my spirits.

'Tell us about the practice of, er, flagellatio, Mr P. What exactly do you understand by the term?'

I shifted my position on the hard bench. Delicately I nudged Marian's arm. There was no response. I had to dig her quite hard in the ribs before I could get her attention.

'Would you like to go?' I whispered, pointing towards the door to make matters clearer.

'No, thank you, dear. I went before lunch if you recall.'

She turned placidly back to the action. Again I prodded her and asked if she didn't feel the proceedings were too ... well ... warm? No, she said, she was perfectly comfortable. Did she not feel, I hissed, that the case was indecent? This time understanding dawned. Marian reached out and with a kindly gesture covered my hand with her own. She had forgotten how young I was, she said. If I felt uncomfortable I was to go right on ahead and she would meet me outside the court at the end of the afternoon. 'For at my age, dear,' she said with an amused gleam in her eye, 'I'm way past being corrupted. I must say, though, that in all my time I never had a chance to learn so many new things in one afternoon.'

Feeling I had done all I could to protect my guest from moral damage, I sat back and joined her in the drive towards self-education and was asked no more questions until the court rose at the end of the day.

'You know,' Marian sighed as we made our way out of court afterwards. 'I feel quite regretful to have to fly on to Denmark tomorrow. I feel that my stay here in London has been far too short.'

We pushed out through the courtroom doors to find the corridor unexpectedly thronged with people. Spectators pouring from the court next door conglomerated into a living mass humming and swirling towards the stairs. Necks craned eagerly to catch a glimpse of celebrities making for the exit flanked by swarms of pressmen. Caught in the charged atmosphere, we too elbowed forward, straining like starving beggars for the sight of a famous ear or half a celebrated nose as these momentarily surfaced from the boiling pot only to be swallowed up again.

'Oh, Charlotte, look!' Marian seized my arm in a clamp-like grip and pointed. Framed in the court doorway in wig and gown stood none other than the chauvinist of lunchtime, looking as offensively lofty as ever.

'Lord's sakes, what an amazing coincidence,' exclaimed Marian, waving.

'There's Gerald Dodgwick now,' said one of the press behind us. 'Think he'll give us a quote?'

97

'No way,' said another. 'Toffee-nosed bugger.'

They moved away. I stood bolted to the spot, feeling my feet going red inside my barristerial pumps. Gerald Dodgwick? Upward spread the hideous blush to my knees, front, back and sides, until every part of me beamed fluorescent pink with shame. Unable to look up, I stared at the mosaic pattern on the floor. I would have liked to sink through it and spend the rest of my life down among the laths.

'I really do apologize, Charlotte dear,' I heard Marian saying from a long way off. Why was she apologizing to me? Surely I ought to be begging her pardon after all she had been through? I looked up. My guest appeared to be suffering from some kind of mental strain. Her face had a fixed and anxious expression; her fingers were tightly interlaced and her shoulders shook. 'I'm just so sorry,' she said again, and sitting down on a bench gave way to laughter – no mere genteel giggling but great racking gusts of hilarity which shook her slight frame back and forth like a ragdoll. I stood watching in perplexity, then suddenly to my surprise found that I was in the same state. Side by side, while the last of the crowd melted away down the staircase and the Royal Courts of Justice settled into silence around us, Marian Crockford and I sat on the bench and laughed and laughed.

9

'Damn it, Freddy, it's an ... impertinence.' Jim Harbutt paced back and forth across the carpet like a caged beast. 'I'm forced to admit it; I take this personally. I feel most insulted, to be perfectly frank.'

He took a sharp turn around the corner of Freddy's desk which brought the toe of his shoe into sudden loud contact with the wastepaper bin.

'That's right,' said Freddy faintly. 'Don't stint yourself. Bring the room down around our ears if it'll relieve your feelings.'

'Sorry. No, but, joking aside, I'll make no secret of the fact that I think it's pretty poor form.' He attacked his shaggy hair with a wild hand. 'In fact, I think it's a bugger and I don't mind who hears me say so.'

'In the circumstances that's just as well,' said my pupilmaster. 'There's no need to roar, my dear chap. I'm not stone deaf, at least I wasn't until quite recently.'

'Oh, did I raise my voice? Sorry, I didn't notice. The fact is,' said Jim, breathing hard, '... and I don't mind admitting it to you, Freddy: this thing's got me a bit ... nettled.' He stopped before the great desk and glared down his nose in a basilisk fashion. 'Well, Freddy, what do you say? Is it or is it not a damned impertinence?'

Freddy got up and strolled towards the fireplace. 'Well, you know, from a High Court judge to a man of ... what are you, three years' call, I hardly think I'd call it an impertinence exactly,' he said in a considering tone.

'What would you call it then?'

'I think I'd be inclined to call it a reprimand.'

There was a sound of grinding teeth. 'With the greatest respect, Freddy, I don't believe you can have absorbed it properly. I think I'd better read it you again. Damn, where did I put the thing?'

'You cast it into the rubbish bin, as I recall.'

'Did I? Oh yes, so I did. Quite right, here it is.' He picked out a crumpled ball of paper and smoothed it flat. 'Now, as I say, listen to this . . .'

'I've already heard it through at least twice, dear boy,' said Freddy. 'Oh well, if you really must . . .'

'Dear Harbutt . . .' Jim read grimly:

'When you appeared before me this morning I could not help but be struck by the extremely odd headdress you were wearing, which I presume may have been intended to pass for a barrister's wig. No doubt others may already have done so, but I nevertheless felt myself in duty bound to point out to you that to appear in court in such eccentric dress can only give the sort of impression that should be avoided. I am naturally concerned that no slur should be cast upon the reputation of my old chambers. Yours, etc.

Dodwell

'It really astonishes me,' said Jim explosively, 'that a man of Dodwell's stamp, and presumably intellect, should even be bothered with something so footling as matters of appearance and dress. No mention, you'll notice, of how I handled the case, and I did feel that my submission had been, well, quite powerful, to say the least. "Eccentric", . . . well really, I ask you.'

'No good asking me anything until I've seen the offending headpiece, dear boy,' said Freddy. 'Why not go away and put it on? Then young Charlotte here and I will be able to give you our views.'

Struck by the good sense of this, Jim went off; his heavy breathing could be heard receding down the hallway.

Freddy looked after him, oyster eyes bright with amusement. 'Now, young Hunter, what about that advice you're still doing over there? Will it prove to have been your life's work, do you think?'

'I'm almost sure of it,' I said, looking out over the wall of books heaped on my desk. 'The queer thing is that the problem seemed simple until I brought the law into it; now I'm floundering.'

'Bringing the law into anything at the expense of common sense is a great mistake,' pronounced my pupilmaster, taking off his reading glasses and pointing them at me. 'Use your common sense, young Hunter, if you have any left. What does it tell you?'

'That the defendant ought not to have been keeping stoats in the first place,' I said. 'I don't think anyone should, at least not so many.'

'Although undoubtedly true, that is beside the point, young Hunter. Only one got out and bit the dog.'

'Yes, that's right,' I conceded, 'but I'd rather have had a troupe of tigers in the case than that one stoat.'

'I don't suppose the driver would.'

'No, but tigers are known to be legally fierce; what about stoats? Again, there's the question of whether it could have been foreseen that the dog would jump on the car bonnet and cause the accident . . .'

'There must be some authority,' said Freddy. 'You must use your ingenuity, dear girl. Find something analagous. I'm almost sure there's a case somewhere . . . Try looking under minks, or was it gas? I forget. When all else fails, remember that first impressions are usually reliable. What was yours by the by?'

'I forget.'

'What you need, young Charlotte, is a cup of strong coffee to sharpen your failing wits. We can't have you mentally dropping to pieces all over the place; you know what a stickler I am for orderliness. We shall attend to your needs in a moment. In the meantime . . . What's this? Great merciful heavens.'

A spectacular sight had appeared in the doorway.

An ordinary barrister's wig lies modestly flat on the wearer's head, showing a certain amount of his hair, if he has any. This thing, however, was close-fitting at the bottom like a bearskin helmet, with high sides rising into a dome ornamented by a cascade of grey curls, puffs, tuckets and horsehair whirls from beneath which Jim's aquiline face peeped like a crow in an Easter bonnet. The structure lacked the spaniel ears of a full-bottomed wig but perhaps over-compensated for this by tapering down into a number of longish tails tied with neat black bows which dangled coyly here and there about his shoulders.

Freddy's face as he regarded the apparition was a well-ordered blank. Gravely he asked to be shown the back. Jim obediently twirled around and the tails floated out around him like ribbons on a maypole. Slowly Freddy advanced a few paces, still intently regarding the thing, seemed about to poke it, then apparently changed his mind.

'Just one query, if I may,' he murmured at his most urbane. 'Is it dead, do you know, or merely resting?' Then his lip twitched. He sat down on the edge of the desk and began to laugh. Jim from beneath his lush curls looked out at us with a homicidally fierce expression which only made matters worse.

'I do beg your pardon, James,' Freddy said when he was able to speak. 'I wouldn't for the world hurt your feelings, but really, you know, if you could see yourself . . .' He drew out a silk handkerchief and wiped his eyes. 'I believe it's those pigtails,' he said, 'or tentacles, or whatever they are, whirling around like that. No, now I think about it I can't make up my mind whether it's the tails or the body. Do turn round, my dear chap, just once more.'

But Jim refused to oblige and stood rooted to the carpet, stiff with outrage. 'I take it I've had your answer?' he said rather frigidly.

'Answer? My dear fellow, what other answer could there possibly be? You'll have to go up to Ede & Ravenscroft and buy yourself a wig; nothing else for it.'

'But I only bought this the day before yesterday,' objected Jim. 'I've only had it on once.'

'And that was once too often, by the sound of things.'

'Well, be that as it may, it cost me a damned arm and a leg – seventy-five pounds, no less.'

'It can't be helped,' said Freddy. 'I'm sorry to hear it, but you know it's not going to improve matters to throw away your reputation as well as your money. You asked my advice and you can take it from me that that thing . . .' He glanced at it again and then quickly averted his eyes as if to avoid offending Jim still further by another attack of laughter. 'I should go today. In fact, if I were you I'd go at once. Get one off the peg second-hand if you can. You can't afford to go before old Dodders again looking like a comedy turn. He'd commit you for contempt of court, not to mention the question of bringing the bar into disrepute. No, but really, my dear fellow, just look at it . . .'

Here Freddy made the mistake of doing so himself and instantly dissolved into mirth once more.

Jim gave a snort of exasperation and had turned to leave when David Jermaine and Bill Armstrong appeared in the doorway, presumably making a whistle-stop on the way to the Coffee Shoppe.

'Oh, good God,' said Jermaine. 'I'm to be Queen of the May, mother –'

'Whoops, kiss me Hardy,' squawked Bill Armstrong and went off to bring others from neighbouring rooms to see the circus.

'And now,' said Jim, looking round at his persecutors, who must by that time have been eight or nine in number, 'if you've all had your fill of entertainment, I think I'll go and get on with some work.' Stiffly he made his way back to the doorway, to find that once more his escape was blocked. Standing there this time was William Bradbury, chambers' most senior member, affectionately known to all as the Old Bill. Regarding Jim's headwear with interest, the old gentleman slowly advanced into the room and walked round him, inspecting it fixedly from all angles.

'Well, O.B.,' Jim said at last. 'What do you think?'

'I like it,' said Bradbury with decision. 'Vintage George IV, I'd have said. Am I right? Yes, I thought so. Quite a good example of its kind. Where did you come by that? Not at Ede & Ravenscroft, I'll be bound.'

Jim Harbutt's face had lit up with a delighted smile. 'There you are, you see,' he said to the rest of us. 'The cognoscenti, like Old Bill here, can tell the genuine article at a glance. I was lucky enough to come across it in an antique shop in Romford, where I was reliably informed that this actual wig you see here might have been worn at the royal court.'

'Quite possibly,' the old gentleman concurred. 'On state occasions, one would imagine.'

'Well, O.B., it's lucky you came in,' said Jim, sweeping the thing off his head with a look of triumph. 'These philistines here have been saying . . .'

'Oh, before you take it off,' said Bradbury, disappointed, 'why don't you let us see the rest of the costume? What's it for, by the way: a fancy-dress ball, or are the Inn putting on a pageant . . .?'

It was some time after lunch on the same day, as I was still trying to clear my desk of the stoats, that young Paul the clerk put his head round the door. 'Miss Hunter, you haven't seen Mr Tobin by any chance?' His pale blue eyes probed the corners, the curtains and the area under the table. 'He wouldn't be about here at all, I suppose?'

'I'm afraid not,' I said. 'He went out at about one and I haven't seen him since.'

'Not still at lunch, is he? Oh gawd.'

I looked at my watch. 'I shouldn't think so. It's almost four o'clock.'

'You didn't happen to notice who he was with?'

'Well he did say something about meeting Mr Jermaine at the Cock, I think.'

'That's cooked it,' said Paul. It struck me that our junior clerk was looking almost animated.

'Is anything the matter?' I asked.

'His conference is here: Mr Lamb, senior partner of Lamb Griffin, with a client. Norman's gone over the road and Mr Tobin's disappeared. And Mr Lamb doesn't like to be kept waiting – at least, I don't expect he'll like it.' He fiddled with his broad tie, tightening it in his nervous abstraction so that the knot, instead of hanging in the area of his breastbone, rose almost to the level of his collar. I had never seen a senior partner but it was clear that they were a force to be reckoned with.

'Oh, wait a second, is that him coming?' His face went slack with relief. 'It's Mr Tobin, thank God for that. Oh, there you are, sir, you're here. Your con's here. Mr Lamb, sir, he's here for your four o'clock con. The client's here too. Are you ready? Shall I bring them in?'

Freddy stemmed this tide of eloquence with an uplifted hand and made his way to his desk. At the sight of his reassuring presence Paul seemed to unfold like a spring leaf, loosening his tie again as he set about the task of arranging two leather chairs and an ashtray before Freddy's desk in a slipshod manner far more like his normal self.

'Shall I wheel them in, sir?' he asked again, as though just a trifle apprehensive that my pupilmaster might refuse to accept delivery.

Barely waiting to receive a nod, Paul was out of the room, closing the door carefully behind him, presumably in order to be able to knock upon it with proper ceremony when he came back with the clients.

This he did within a matter of moments. On being bidden to enter, he reverently opened the door, ushered in the clients and crept with them across the room in such an obsequious manner that it would have been no surprise to see him offer to carry the senior partner the short distance on his back. The thought was made more ridiculous by the size of Mr Lamb, who resembled a soapstone Buddha dressed in large quantities of tailored navy suiting. A thick gold watch-chain stretched taut across an impressive paunch and gold links studded his cuffs. It was plain that, in every sense, Mr Lamb had wool on his back. The lay client, by contrast, was a younger man, thin with a droopy moustache and Slavic cheekbones which stood out in dramatic relief from a face full of dark hollows.

'Mr Tobin,' said the solicitor in a voice like simnel cake, 'may I introduce Mr Firoulescou?'

Freddy inclined his head graciously to each. I noticed that, although I had stood up, Freddy remained still, perhaps in order to remind Mr Lamb who was in charge of the proceedings. Majestically he raised a hand and motioned both to be seated. Obediently solicitor and client sank into the leather chairs on either side of the great desk and waited.

Freddy's preparations for this conference seemed unusually meticulous. First he withdrew from his breast pocket a gold propelling pencil; having carefully adjusted the lead to his liking, he laid it down on the tooled leather blotter. Next he brought out a matching fountain pen, which he filled before setting it down beside the pencil. Opening a desk drawer, he replaced the ink bottle and took up a slim sheaf of paper, which he arranged before him. Then, placing the fingertips of both hands together, he raised his eyebrows slightly in a gesture of invitation and waited in the manner of an oracle to be addressed by his clients. As a piece of stage timing it was tremendously impressive. Although I had by now watched my pupilmaster hypnotize clients on quite a number of occasions, I had not until now realized that his capabilities ran to overawing them without speaking a word. The Lord Chancellor in all his robes could not have conveyed a greater impression of magnificence.

Seeming to feel that he had received his cue, Mr Lamb leaned forward in his chair. 'Mr Tobin,' he said in his rich voice. 'As you will no doubt recall from your perusal of the papers in this case, Mr Firoulescou has recently undertaken what might appropriately be styled a rash venture into matrimony. His purpose in consulting you is to clarify his mind as to the most apposite course to be pursued with a view to the speedy termination of what may, I think, be regarded as a voidable marriage, and further with a view to the expeditious resolution of such financial aspects as may be involved. I trust that has simplified matters. Now, Mr Firoulescou, be so good as to put Mr Tobin in possession of the facts, if you will.'

I picked up my pencil to take notes. The client tossed back his dark mane and bent a brooding gaze upon a small flaw in the ceiling.

'Ah, what can I say? I am without words, without words,' he cried.

For several minutes after that we waited while Mr Firoulescou moodily regarded the chandelier, obviously grappling with strong emotions. I was trying to guess how much per hour this conference must be costing him when Mr Lamb, who had apparently been following the same train of thought, remarked in a bracing manner, 'Come along, Mr Firoulescou. Time's money, you know.'

This treatment, while it struck me as a little brisk, nevertheless seemed to have the required effect of helping the client to master his feelings, for he suddenly roused himself and shot through the starting gate into a tangled monologue. One thing became clear. Mr Firoulescou had been wrong in thinking himself to be without words. Indeed, words puffed out of him as though he were a bubble-pipe, until the room seemed full of them, spinning and whirling about in the draught stirred up by his restless hands. The speech was made harder to follow by the fact that much of it was in a guttural foreign tongue, and it was impressive how effortlessly Freddy seemed to be able to piece the narrative together without interrupting the flow, merely nodding from time to time to signal comprehension.

The story sounded less like real life than the plot of a romantic novelette, and although some of this could be ascribed to Mr Firoulescou's qualities as a storyteller there could be no doubt that the case was unusual. He was, he said, a naturalized emigré from what had once been Moldavia. At an embassy function one evening he had been introduced to a young woman member of the Russian legation to whom he had quickly found himself attracted.

'It was like a thunderblast,' said the client throatily, illustrating the effect of the experience by smiting himself on the forehead with a clenched fist. 'I asked myself, Vica, why do you perspire? Why do you wheeze? Why does your heart rattle and thump so fast?'

As he described these alarming symptoms, Mr Firoulescou's face lit up with a reminiscent smile. 'Ah yes, these things I asked myself, yet all the time I knew. It was –' he confided in a reverent whisper, 'loff.'

Mr Lamb cleared his throat and took refuge in the file of correspondence on his knee. I looked to see what Freddy was making of these revelations. He, however, was betraying no sign of unease but sat as before with his elbows on the desk, hands lightly clasped, regarding the client with the look of a confessor.

Having met his fate in this way, it was only a matter of weeks before Mr Firoulescou found himself at the Kensington District Registry plighting his troth. He had been, as he put it, swept to the altar by tides of loff. Following the brief ceremony, the amorous waters had washed him round the corner to a local hotel, where a celebration was held 'with much sinking and clock-dancing of our homeland'. From his description of it, the reception had been extremely long. He had passed the time agreeably, he told us, watching his wife take part in the various clog-dances, and apparently dividing his thoughts between satisfaction at the envy of other men that he had become the possessor of such a pearl and apprehension about the probable cost of the reception in terms of a fireplace full of shattered glassware alone. He had been anticipating, he remarked, the coming of the dark.

'What shall I tell you of my thoughts as I lay waiting beneath the bedcloths?' cried the client. 'I was as a lion . . .' He spread bony fingers over his knees and stretched his thin neck towards the ceiling. 'I was as a bull,' he added, in case we had missed his drift. 'I was . . .'

'Hold hard, Mr Firoulescou. That's to say, steady on,' said the solicitor hastily. 'Ladies present, you know.'

Baffled, I was beginning to look about for signs of stowaways when I realized that Mr Lamb must be referring to myself. Kindly meant though it was, this piece of chivalry put me in a difficulty: to look embarrassed was out of the question, but as a lady to look unembarrassed might suggest lewd curiosity. Flustered, and annoyed with myself for it, I went through a series of head and hand gestures intended to convey some form of professional detatchment, but which were more likely to have given the impression that I was mentally below par.

When at last she came out of the bathroom, said Mr Firoulescou, he had noticed with surprise that his rosebud was dressed for their first night together in a long flannel nightshirt with a corset on top, a football jersey, at least one pair of woollen tights, long bottle-green socks and an overcoat.

'I asked myself, Vica, what is this? And although to you perhaps it may seem droll,' said Mr Firoulescou, eyeing Freddy as though suspicious that his air of sympathetic calm might suddenly disintegrate into lunatic mirth, 'to me, I assure you, it was no such thing. In fact, Mr Tobin, I will speak frankly, I suspected from that moment that all was not well.'

He gave a dispirited sigh which blew the ends of his long moustache outwards. As his new wife clambered into bed in all her paraphernalia, he said, he had gone under some pretext to think in the bathroom. Psychology had quickly shown him the answer. What ailed his wife was surely maiden modesty. He must show her that this quality, although undoubtedly a virtue to be prized in a young unmarried girl, was less praiseworthy in a wife. How was this to be done? Again psychology came to his aid. His first step must be to show that he was not a beast but a person of refined feelings. Suddenly he hit upon a most effective way of reassuring his swaddled spouse – an idea so masterly that it was with high hopes of success that he went back to bed, to spend what could only be called an unusual wedding night. 'For, to set her mind at rest, I myself,' said the client, 'wore a mackintosh.'

Most of the honeymoon had been spent in Calais, which seemed a curious choice until Mr Firoulescou explained that they had been delayed there owing to his having run into an articulated lorry on the quay while looking out for signposts to Paris. Despite this disappointing start, they had passed the days pleasantly enough; the weather had been fine and there had been enough of interest to see and eat in the town. But the nights . . . The client shook his head: hot aching deserts of time in which the bride in her overcoat and he in his mackintosh lay sweltering side by side like canelloni in an oven dish.

By and by, however, he began to see his patience rewarded. On the second night his wife discarded the socks; on the third the football jersey went. On the fourth evening Mr Firoulescou once again resorted to psychology. What could this mean, he reasoned, but that his rosebud was now ready to be unfurled? Were these subtle signals not designed to tell him that she now wanted him to show that he was a man? This was what intuition told him; now was the moment. He must be swift though, he must leap. Any delay might make his wife feel rejected and undo all the good work of the past three days. Mr Firoulescou leapt. He had got rid of the overcoat and nightshirt and was working on the corset when his wife's maiden modesty again came to the fore. Mr Firoulescou took refuge in the bathroom with a black eye and heavy bruising to other parts. After a miserable night locked in this hiding place, he had been forced to conclude that something was fundamentally wrong with his marriage. He no longer believed, he said, that his wife had married him for love.

'In short,' said the solicitor, 'a marriage of convenience on the part of the wife aimed at obtaining British nationality, and a fairly classic case, as I'm sure you will agree, Mr Tobin. And I think it is correct to say, is it not, Mr Firoulescou, that the marriage has never been consummated? That's to say you have never . . . um . . .?'

Mr Firoulescou shook his head. 'After that I tried no more to consume it. The marriage is,' he said sadly, 'a skeleton.'

'I have naturally advised Mr Firoulescou that he would be entitled to seek a decree of nullity on the grounds of wilful refusal to consummate. As I understand it, however, he takes the view that an allegation of non-consummation would reflect badly on his, er, prowess.'

'I should be a laughing stick.'

'Er, precisely so. I have of course explained to Mr Firoulescou the practical advantages of a decree of nullity as opposed to one of divorce, from the financial and every other aspect. Well, it's self-evident. One need hardly . . . You do understand, don't you, Mr Firoulescou: you do not want to recognize that this marriage exists.'

'But I do,' said the client surprisingly. 'I wish to consume the marriage. My question is: how am I to do this?'

'I hardly feel that you can ask Mr Tobin to advise you about that,' said the solicitor. 'Besides, I recall that during our discussions last week you said you could see no prospect of her consenting to, er, assist you in the consummation of this marriage?'

'Yes, but now I do not know in which direction to jump,' said Mr Firoulescou, looking rather wildly round the room as though about to launch himself off like a grasshopper. 'If I nullify this woman, all is at an end between us, yet if not, I let her have her will of me and take British nationality by a trick. Po, po, po.'

With this last observation he got to his feet and began pacing the carpet, deep in thought. Freddy made no move to interrupt his deliberations and for a short time a silence fell, which after the verbose hour or so we had been through was very restful, broken only by the occasional 'po, po, po' or stronger affirmative 'pa, pa, pa'.

'Pa, pa, pa . . . But what if I say, "Irena, if you do not agree to live with me as a wife, sadly I have no choice . . ." The client stopped dead in his tracks. Surely I must be mistaken in believing that on that dark and tragic face there was dawning the ghost of a wicked grin . . . "Unhappily, I have no choice," I say. "If you do not agree, I must have the marriage nullified, so that in law it has never been. Then for you . . . no British nationality; quick export to Moscow." Pa, pa, pa . . .'

Mr Firoulescou spun on his heel to face Freddy's desk and held up his clasped hands in a gesture of victory. 'The door is clear,' he cried. 'At last. I am decided; I am resolute. Ah, Mr Tobin, you have been a great help to me. You have been wonderful. All that Mr Lamb has said of you is true . . .'

Rising to follow his client from the room, Mr Lamb shook Freddy's hand in a satisfied manner. 'Rather an emotional fellow,' he remarked with disapproval. 'Still, you sorted him out admirably. I'll look forward to our next meeting.'

'Great pleasure,' said my pupilmaster. 'Glad to have been able to help.'

It was the first time since the beginning of the conference that he had been heard to speak.

'That was fascinating,' I said to Freddy when they had gone. 'I was particularly interested in the way you approached it – letting the client feel that he'd worked the decision out for himself, so to speak. I must say, there's a lot to learn as a pupil. I thought you were terribly effective.'

My pupilmaster had reseated himself at his desk, eyes closed, head in hands.

'Rather a heavy lunch,' he said faintly. 'Went all right, did it? I'm afraid at the moment I can't remember much about it. Be a good girl and bring me a strong cup of coffee . . .'

10

'More Irish stew, Gerda? I believe there is some barley and a bone left. Any bids for this last spoonful of broad beans?'

'In Iran we eat too much this beans,' remarked Hasan. 'But first we must take all the clothes off.'

'What, everything, Hasan?' Mrs Gossage sounded mildly scandalized.

'Yes, madaam, otherwise is no good.'

'That would be some sort of . . . native ceremony, I suppose?' said his hostess doubtfully. 'Would it be to do with religion; to symbolize coming to the table in a state of purity perhaps?'

'No, madaam. Is because e-jackets are too tough,' explained Hasan, pointing to a row of what looked like small polythene bags discarded on his plate. 'My e-mader he take off all the clothes. After he froy in best botter and roll in hoigh-quality roice, then he lie under the sheep's leg in pot in oven for very long toime. In this way he turn into baghali pollo, all best quality.'

'Yes, well, it all sounds very nice, Hasan,' said Mrs Gossage. 'I expect you enjoy it very much?'

'No, madaam. Is harrible.' Hasan dismissed all his mother's heroic efforts at a stroke. 'But my e-fader she loike too much this thing. One time she e-burst her trouser. And now she is not any more thin; she is . . . patapouf.' He sketched a balloon shape in the air and blew out his cheeks dramatically.

'I myself,' said Mrs Gossage confidentially, 'have been a martyr to the same thing. Your father, or was it your mother, should try charcoal biscuits, Hasan, in my opinion. Now if everyone has finished I'll just bring up the seconds, if someone wouldn't mind stacking the plates.'

She rose and bustled away. I wondered if it might be treacle tart, or jam sponge and custard.

'Now, which of you here has visited the Chamber of Horrors

at Madame Tussaud's? Nils, have you? You really should, you know; there is much to be seen . . .'

Yes, he was right, I thought: there was much to be seen and, for that matter, done – most of it outside the walls of this railway-brown womb. I was beginning to feel something was missing from my life; a certain amount of dash and sparkle would not go amiss.

'. . . Then there was the well-known poisoner Dr Crippen. Ah, here comes Mrs Gossage with the dessert. And what do you propose to regale us with this evening, my dear?'

'I hope you will all like our English bread pudding,' said Mrs Gossage. 'We in England are fond of it with cold custard . . .'

As though a guillotine had come down between the old life and the new, my time at the Gossages' hostel was suddenly over. I was as good as gone. Little did she suspect that, by the time she sat down and spread out her napkin once more, Mrs Gossage had begun receding into history. Goodbye, Mrs Gossage. Goodbye, brown dim kitchen with the polypropylene curtains; the time has come for us to part. Goodbye, cabbage smell and red rubber tuberoses. Suddenly I had a vision of myself as a flat-dweller, in a tea-gown perhaps, drooped gracefully over the parapet of a penthouse balcony, enjoying the jewelled tapestry of a night city by moonlight . . .

The flat-sharing market was depressed. Everywhere I went, clutching my little card from one or other of the agencies there was something not quite right: the flat was too small or too grubby; far from the underground station or on top of it; just next to a bonemeal refinery, or damp like one particular place I had visited in the incredibly named Vale of Health where a spread of poison-pink toadstools made the lounge carpet resemble an aerial view of Benidorm beach.

After a few weeks I decided that I was being too demanding. From now on I would adopt a more positive approach, be open-minded, ready to see the brighter side of things. Carried along by enthusiasm, I could make flat-hunting if not pleasurable and worthwhile, at least a tolerable experience. It was in this spirit of determined optimism that I started up the stairs one early September afternoon towards the dingy offices of Pads Unlimited Ltd, behind Paddington Station.

The girl behind the desk balanced her bottle of nail varnish on the top of a nearby typewriter and carefully lowered the brush into it using the balls of finger and thumb to avoid smudging the newly painted lacquer. Her nails were crimson icicles. Using both hands she moved a dirty coffee cup and a half-full bottle of milk aside and turned to me a world-weary little face immobile with makeup. A waft of air from the moving electric fan on the wall momentarily lifted her false eyelashes. Her lipsticked mouth, pink as a bitten fig, stirred in recognition but did not smile.

'I'm afraid I don't think there's been anything in since last week that would interest you,' she said, waving one hand in the air, then stopping to examine the varnish.

'What, nothing at all? Are you sure?'

'Well, I don't remember anything; nothing that would suit you anyway.'

'How do you mean, that would suit me?' I asked, tantalized.

'Well, you know, suitable.'

'Why's that?'

'What?'

'Why do you think nothing's come in? Isn't that unusual?'

'The market's depressed,' the girl said, as though repeating a lesson and looking as if the malaise were catching on. She examined the other hand and blew thoughtfully on the fingertips.

'No,' she said after a minute. 'If there'd been anything, I think I'd have remembered.'

'While I'm here, I wonder if you'd mind just checking up? I am a bit desperate.'

'Checking up?'

'Well, just having a look through your cards in case.'

The girl stared at me as though I had suggested she jog up to Birmingham and back. Slowly she removed a dirty teacup from the top of a small box file and drew it towards her.

'Quen-tin,' she called to a wispy youth at a desk on the other side of the room on which were spread some dogeared folders and a small picnic. 'What happened to Oak Street. Has it gone?'

'Search me, duck,' said the young man, crunching into a stick of celery. 'Either filled or fallen down by now. Oh, I say, the tomato's made the poppyseed roll all mushy.'

The girl flipped open the lid of the box file and began flicking through the cards inside, parting them with delicate pincer movements of her talons. Her lips moved silently as she read. I noticed that many of the cards were worn and dusty – presumably in keeping with the accommodation they offered.

'Bilton Road, you went to see that, didn't you? It says here a nice big room, share bathroom and kitchen, use of garden. Sounds nice.'

'Dogs,' I said.

'It says here, "Dog-lover preferred". Weren't you told?'

'It ought to say, "Dog preferred".'

'Why, aren't you a dog lover?' She shot me a suspicious glance.

'Look,' I said, 'it's one thing being a dog lover; living in a kennel is quite another. By the way, I'd say from the smell of that place that use of garden was definitely *not* allowed.'

'Mm,' said the girl. 'Quen-tin, has Maida Vale gone?'

'Ask me another, lovey,' said Quentin, popping in a chocolate fancy.

The girl drew out another card. 'Sydenham Terrace. "Nice big garden flat", etc. Sounds super.'

'It was rather like a Turkish bath,' I said.

'Steamy, was it?' The girl looked blank.

'The place was full of men . . . wearing towel wraps, nothing else.'

'Perhaps you went too early in the morning, while they were still getting washed?'

'That's hardly the point. Anyway the whole place smelled of smoked teabags; it was hardly for them to object to my smoking cigarettes . . .'

'Oh, I didn't know about that,' said the girl. 'I'd better note it down . . . non-smoker preferred.'

'I shouldn't send anyone there if I were you,' I said. 'Not if they're looking for a decent flat. In my opinion that was an indecent flat. I could hardly feel at home with all those half-naked men drifting about.'

'You'll have to get with it, you know,' said the girl. 'Mixed flats are all the rage these days. The thing now is for both sexes to muck in together . . . As they say in America, let it all hang out.'

'That's just the point, it was,' I said. 'Look, if you do get something more respectable in, could you let me know? I can't stay where I am much longer; I'm being starved to death.'

The girl opened her eyes as wide as the eyelashes permitted and surveyed me up and down.

'I promise you,' she said, 'nobody would ever guess.'

I shook the dust of Pads Unlimited Ltd from my feet for ever and went back to chambers.

With a feeling of homecoming I pushed open the hissing inner door and heard teatime sounds coming today from the direction of Mike Deacon's room. As I approached, snatches of conversation reached me above the general babble. I could make out the foghorn note of the walrus, obviously recounting some joke, for a particularly loud blast was followed by laughter and allegations from Owen Ap William that he was a whiskery old imposter, which seemed to please the walrus considerably, judging by the appreciative volley of barks and leathery smacks which ensued. It seemed that David Jermaine had had his hair cut, giving rise, as always on these occasions, to a good deal of ribbing about coots and billiard balls and whether baldness was a sign of sexual prowess, making me wonder – not for the first time – if underneath it all men were not simple creatures at heart.

'Actually, I don't mind admitting I was rather pleased at the way my cross-examination came out.' Graham's voice rose enthusiastically from the mêlée. 'Yes, I will have a chocolate biscuit, thanks, Paul . . . I'd been charged with attempted theft from the person; alleged to have held up my handbag as a kind of screen to hide my hand going into the victim's coat pocket . . . you know the form. I was a woman of about thirty-five and a bit of a pro: special pocket in my skirt; a false-bottomed old bag.'

'Graham, you seem to have a remarkably intimate knowledge of your female clients, if one may venture to say so.'

'Don't be such a vulgarian, David,' said Graham in disgust. 'Now you've made me forget what I was saying. Oh yes, about the victim. In cross-examination I elicited from him that he knew for certain that his pockets were completely empty, you see; there was no way my client could have got anything. Nearly got her off on a submission of no case. I was pretty chuffed actually.'

'Who the hell was on the bench?' asked Bill Armstrong. 'Must have been a twit, whoever he was.'

'What do you mean, nearly got her off?' said Jim Harbutt. 'Did you actually get her off or not?'

'Well, not exactly, in the sense that they went against me ultimately; she in fact got a twelve-month suspended sentence, but when I argued the proposition that you can't attempt what is impossible I had the distinct feeling that the bench was leaning in my direction.'

'You're lucky it didn't fall down on top of you like a ton of bricks if that's what you were arguing,' said Bill Armstrong roundly. 'The authorities are absolutely dead against you.'

'What about the case of *Collins*? The facts there were four-square with this one of mine,' objected Graham.

'But that was ancient!'

'Well, 1864, if you call that ancient.'

'Of course I do. It's just as I thought. There was a modern authority on much the same facts. I forget the name now.'

'*Ring*,' supplied Jim, who had been leafing through *Archbold*. 'Attempt to pick an empty pocket, 1892.'

'There you are. Told you so.'

'Did you appear in that case, Bill?' Mike Deacon beat a swift retreat into the corner. With a fortieth birthday at the end of the month, Armstrong was known to be touchy on the subject of age.

'I think you'll find,' said Armstrong, ignoring the interruption, 'that it was decided there that impossibility was no defence, overruling your case of *Collins* or whatever it was.'

'Right,' Jim said. 'There's another case here of an attempt to have sex with a duck. Same thing: "relative physical impossibility" no defence.'

'Relative?' Owen Ap William drained his teacup. 'If you ask me, the thing's a complete impossibility. Great heaven, the Lord Chief himself couldn't manage it.'

'Well, frankly I think the position is less than satisfactory,' said Graham with some heat.

'Your feelings do you credit, Graham,' said Jermaine, entering into the spirit of this. 'And a perplexing experience for the duck . . .'

'What I meant was,' resumed Graham, 'that if that's the law of this country it's entirely illogical. Good lord, if people are to be prosecuted for allegedly trying to do the impossible, it's only a step between that and making it an offence to have thoughts of doing something illegal or immoral.'

'In which case, David could be classed as a recidivist,' said Haliburton's room-mate Timothy Crowe from behind the tea-urn.

'The tone of this establishment gets worse every day,' said

Jermaine. 'Nothing but low abuse and loose ducks. I think I'll go back to my room for a good sleep.'

'Speaking for myself,' said Freddy, 'I'd find it hard to think of a duck as more than a friend. Ah, Charlotte, back again? Rehoused, I hope?'

'Oh, I'd better not say what I was going to if there are ladies present,' Bill Armstrong said.

'Oh, this is no lady; this is my pupil,' Freddy assured him. 'And, speaking of that, young Hunter, I've just sent an advice of yours out for typing with only a few minor alterations. Case of Winterton? Webster? Anyway, quite a nice piece of work. Are you all right, dear girl, you look a little pale all of a sudden . . .'

Shortly after this Freddy went off to Star Yard to examine a pair of silver candlesticks. I had been sitting at my desk for half an hour musing delightedly on the glorious position I had reached – of having had an advice of mine sent for typing – when Phil wandered into the room.

'Hello,' he said, looking over my shoulder. 'What are we drowsing over so busily? Not work surely?'

'Oh, worse,' I said. 'Listen to this: "2 prof. m. o/r s/h". It's not English, it's gobbledygook. Then it says, "Selective sharing". What can that be, do you think?'

'Sounds vaguely immoral, whatever it is,' said Phil. 'Sharing what? Who with? Oh, I see. If you're thinking of moving, I'd say that selective sharing of a flat's one thing; if it's beds, make sure it's you doing the selecting. Where are you living now, by the way?'

'North London.'

'Oh, North London?' I might have said Greenland. 'You'll be wanting to move as a matter of urgency then, I can see that.'

'The market's depressed.'

'Never mind about that. At last you have come to the right person.'

'What's this, selective sharing?'

'Not at all. Certainly not,' said Phil with unflattering haste. 'An old girlfriend of mine is looking for someone to share a flat in Knightsbridge. Interested?'

Interested? I could have burst into song. A Knightsbridge flat? By unbelievable luck it seemed that the penthouse of my dreams had suddenly dropped into my lap.

I broke the news to my hosts in North London. They did not precisely crack a bottle of champagne on the spot – that was not their style; but it must be said that they bore the news of our impending parting with remarkable fortitude.

So it was that, on a Sunday afternoon in early October, I found myself standing with all my baggage outside a grimy brown door not far from the Old Brompton Road. From where I stood I could just glimpse the pink minaret of Harrods a few hundred yards away presiding over streets which seemed after Beauchamp Place to deteriorate markedly, so that this entrance was sandwiched between a dry cleaner's and a murky-looking restaurant whose window display featured three stuffed bloaters in need of medical help. In the wall beside the door was an answer-phone grille above a row of buttons and brass cardholders, some empty, some filled with lists of flyblown and faded old tenants. I tried one button, then another. From their dusty grotto the old men of the sea stared out at me in a dispirited manner. After a few minutes a buzzing sound announced that the door had been unlocked and I was able to push my way inside.

The door relocked itself with a snap, leaving me in total darkness. After some groping I found a switch on the wall and by the dim gleam of an overhead bulb saw that I was in a small bare stairwell facing a flight of steps whose nakedness was relieved only by a strip of peeling brown lino probably laid some time between the wars. There was a strange smell of mushrooms. I picked up my cases, wound a giant pink plastic toy snake round my neck like a muffer and began the ascent. The stairs were edged with metal which felt slippery underfoot and once or twice I nearly overbalanced. Halfway up the second flight the light snapped off. I blundered on in darkness, thinking nostalgically of the Gossages. I ought to have known that penthouses at five pounds rent a week were a rarity.

After a long time I became aware of a glimmer of light filtering down from the landing overhead and, gazing up, I saw that it came from a door left ajar. I gained the landing, set down my cases, which had turned to solid ballast at about the second floor, and massaged my cramped fingers to get the feeling back. Then rather hesitantly I tapped on the door. As there was no reply, I pulled my cases over the threshold and looked around. I was in a narrow passageway painted in an indeterminate shade of cream. There was a brownish mustard carpet and the two negative colours together somehow achieved a striking degree of disharmony. A few yards across the passage was another door standing a little way open. I went inside.

It was a room of grand proportions fallen on hard times. The high ceiling, edged by an ornate cornice, was criss-crossed with cracks and shadowed by a sooty deposit which showed in paler outline the laths of the floor above. The carpet was brown; there were a mustard sofa and two armchairs so saggy that the seats bellied almost down to the floor. Against one wall stood a mock-Jacobean dining table and chairs, legs peeling and scuffed with wear. Other furnishings included a very old gas fire, in front of which had been placed a towering electric fire that would have looked at home in the Science Museum, a raffish-looking standard lamp and a print of fishing boats at sunset in a loose wooden frame. At the far end huge windows curtained in dusty brocade gave a panoramic view of the street.

A girl was standing by the window. She had her back to me and all I could tell was that she was as tall as I and built on generous lines. Long black hair was gathered into an untidy knot from which wavy tendrils tumbled down. When she turned her head, my impression was of a vivid face, strikingly made up and presently rather dishevelled. On seeing me, she gave a little squeak and burst into hurried speech.

'Oh, hello, sorry, was that you downstairs? I thought it was the phantom buzzer. Sorry I couldn't come to the door but Jo-jo and I were having a bit of a cuddle, as a matter of fact.'

Slowly there extricated himself from the folds of her clothes a smallish, pale young man, scarcely more than a boy, who stood blinking in the unaccustomed sunlight. For all his looks he must have been a man of some fibre, for he came forward and shook me by the hand with perfect composure before sitting down on the sofa and beginning to comb his hair.

'I'll tell you what,' said the girl. 'I'll be with you in a few minutes. Have a look round, make yourself at home, and I'll come out and show you what's what when we've finished. OK?'

I had not had time to withdraw my head before she had

swooped on Jo-jo again and gathered him up in her arms. He disappeared like a chick into its mother's feathers.

Feeling rather embarrassed to have blundered in upon this tête-à-tête, I wandered down the passageway. The flat was built like a tube with a kind of kink in the middle. There was a corridor from which every so often a door opened off to the left, and as I made my way along I expected any moment to meet the ticket collector. The kink accommodated a small table on which a telephone and a glass coffee jar sat in a frayed nest of papers. I found a bathroom, large and untidy, with every imaginable bottle and jar spilling over onto a floor covered with cracked black and white lino tiles. The bath had ball and claw feet and its grey interior was ringed like a treestump. I caught sight of myself in the mirror and noticed with renewed embarrassment that the pink snake was still wound round my neck. I took it off and carried it into the kitchen. This was a bright room with two windows, one overlooking a panoply of roofs and the other a rubbish chute. I was looking down into a sort of well between the buildings and wondering if I could make a cup of coffee when I heard footsteps approaching and the girl came into the room.

'Hello again, anyway. I'm Maureen Brady. All my friends call me Mo, though, so do. I hope we'll be friends, anyway.'

'I'm sure of it,' I said.

She stood filling the threshold, a fine full-breasted figure dressed in a strange green woolly garment, inexpertly knitted with numerous slubs and unfinished knots in the fabric. Her features were large and well formed, and the total effect was pleasing, although I could not have said whether she was actually pretty – partly because her other qualities somehow reduced the question to insignificance and partly on account of the camouflage effect of her makeup.

'Has Jo-jo gone?' I asked.

'Yes. He's a student at Bristol, you see . . . Oh, my dear little parsnip . . .' She threw both arms round her own waist and hugged herself tightly. 'How am I going to survive a week without you, my lovely boy?' Her arms dropped to her sides. 'I miss him already, you know,' she said. 'Sorry about when you came but when he has to go back to Bristol on a Sunday I simply have to have a good cuddle to keep myself going until Friday, if you know what I mean?'

Not being sure quite what to reply, I nodded enthusiastically.

'It isn't as if we've actually *done* anything – you know, gone all the way,' she hastened to explain. 'Nothing like that.' Her expressive face showed her disgust for weak souls who went all the way. 'No, if there's one thing I can say about myself it's that there's nothing wrong with my morals. I'm quite sound there,' she added, as though going over her points for a prospective purchaser.

'Yes, I'm sure,' I said, thinking that silence might be thought to imply doubt.

'I have to be firm on account of being a believer, you know.'

I wondered if Jo-jo was also a believer.

'Well, yes and no, I suppose,' she said after a moment, her darkly pencilled brows coming together in thought. 'Not in the way of believing there's a god or anything like that. But I always say that everyone's a believer at heart, whether they actually think they believe anything or not. Don't you think so?'

I said I'd never thought of it from that point of view. To be truthful, after the slow and laborious exchange of ideas at the Gossages and the swift badinage of chambers, the vigorous airing of so many fundamental questions at once had winded me rather.

We set off in the direction of the lounge.

'It's nice you've come,' she said suddenly.

'Thanks. I'm glad to be here.'

'Besides,' she said, 'you're big like me. Oh. I didn't mean fat.' She had perhaps detected a consternation in my face of which I instantly felt ashamed. 'There I go again. You mustn't mind me; I'm always putting my foot in it.'

'You're not fat,' I said. 'Not a bit.'

'I'm enormous,' she said mournfully. 'But with Jo-jo away I just seem to stuff myself all the time. Here, talking of that –' She felt in one of the pockets of her dress, or whatever it was. 'Have a peppermint.'

'Thanks very much.'

'No, what I meant to say was, everyone else round here is so, well, dainty; you'll see what I mean.'

'I know exactly what you mean,' I said.

'Have another peppermint. This is your bedroom in here.'

It was a little room overlooking the street. There was a bed, a chair, a small chest of drawers and a place to stand. A strange feature was that the standing area was at the other side of the bed, so that the only way of entering the room was to jump from the doorway onto the bed and roll off the other side. It made for a feeling of informality if anyone dropped in for a chat.

'It's just what I wanted.'

After she had gone, I sat on the bed watching toy cars and buses creeping in the street below. I felt that today marked an important stepping-stone. Whatever the walrus might say, I was now my own man. Ahead of me stretched a flat-dweller's life, full of base temptations, or so I hoped. Soon, too, I would be able to call myself a practising barrister; December and the prospect of my first brief were only a matter of weeks away. Yes, I had come far. I was definitely on the road to fame and fortune.

Goodbye, Mr and Mrs Gossage. Goodbye, Red Manor Students' Residence . . .

And I didn't say au revoir either.

11

Autumn slid down into a damp, chill November. Freddy and I
conducted and won a week-long defended divorce in the High
Court and appeared to advantage in the Court of Appeal. By the
power of our advocacy we obtained injunctions ex parte and inter
partes, requiring respondents to refrain from all kinds of misbe-
haviour ranging from wall-building to wife-beating. We prosecuted a gang of robbers, to the distaste of Freddy, who regarded
crime as inelegant, and making it necessary for him to cheer
himself by buying three silver apostle spoons. I made the notes
and, in addition, to my great pride, had three more pieces of my
work sent out for typing. December came with rain, rushing into
culverts, gushing out, driving, seeping coldly down collars.

At five o'clock one wintry afternoon, the clerks' room was
bedlam. Solicitors, clerks and clients leaving early conferences
jostled in among those arriving for the second sitting. Members of
chambers milled about, wanting to be told why they were doing
this at Aylesbury when they were down in the diary to do that at
Slough; why the application before the master in chambers had
fallen through; and had Norman ironed out that double booking?
Did he think it was possible to get back from an application at
Bedford for a not-before-two over the road unless one had wings,
for God's sake? Stray, uncollected people meandered about like
loose horses, getting underfoot and adding to the crush.
Messengers rushed in and out delivering briefs for the following
day or bearing them off to other chambers. The gas fire blazing
away in the corner of the clerks' room added its mite to the confusion by grilling the coats and trousers of the dry bystanders and
steaming those of the rainsoaked, making the place reek like a
shearing shed. The racket was terrible, and everyone present
howled to be heard above it like souls in torment. In his own
corner young Paul was stamping the post, alternately adding to an
already perilously high pile of envelopes and scurrying away to

conduct clients to conferences. At the eye of the tempest sat Norman, haggard and grey as ever, imperturbably getting on with his work.

As I entered, Paul triumphantly added the last of the post to the pile. It collapsed, spilling forty or so envelopes onto the floor under the milling feet of the crowd. Paul sighed, dropped down on all fours and disappeared into a forest of knees. Just then the walrus opened the door of his private sanctum and stuck his massive head round the lintel. As though the headmaster had appeared, all noise drained from the room. Calmly Percival surveyed the scene. 'Where's Paul?'

With a gesture of the head, Norman indicated the figure on hands and knees now creeping round the fireside corner over the feet of Yardley's senior partner.

'That's the ticket; keep the youngsters busy,' remarked the walrus with approval. 'If he's doing the cleaning, perhaps you'd get me the number of Tyler's chambers, Norman?'

He withdrew his head. Clamour instantly broke out again. With a sigh Norman put down his pencil and three telephone receivers, the diary, a brief and a biscuit and went to fetch the telephone directory. With this opened at the right place, he disappeared into the sanctum. He had hardly reappeared and arranged himself at his desk once more when the massive jowled head appeared again round the door. Again the noise was abruptly hushed.

'Norman,' said the walrus. 'Wrong Tyler.'

Thinking that there ought to be such a plea in English law as justifiable homicide, I watched Norman wordlessly put down two telephone receivers, a set of pleadings, a calendar, a biro and the biscuit and make his way back to the walrus.

I gave a final push forward which brought me to Freddy's pigeonhole. It was empty and I was about to begin shoving my way out again when Norman returned and caught sight of me by the side of his desk.

'Here, Miss Hunter, you might as well take this.'

He dipped a hand into a nearby wire basket and put a thin brief into my hand.

'Thanks, Norman. Is this Mr Tobin's for tomorrow?'

'It's not Mr Tobin's at all,' Norman said. 'Look at it.'

Slowly I turned it over. For one heart-stopping moment I could not believe my eyes.

'For me?' I could feel a huge grin spreading over my face, starting somewhere at the back of my neck. 'Really for me? You're joking.'

'Well, you're a barrister, aren't you, or meant to be?' said Norman. '10.00 a.m. tomorrow, Miss Hunter, and mind you're there by half past nine or I'll have your guts for garters.'

'Yes, right, thanks,' I said. 'Right.'

'Right. Clean shoes, both volumes of *Stone*, a well-brushed suit and a good close shave . . . Well, perhaps we might overlook the last in your case, Miss Hunter, but all the rest applies. No robes, for gawdsakes, it's the magistrates' court. It's down in Kent, so allow plenty of time to spare, as I say, and . . . Oh yes, best of luck.' There was a ghost of a twinkle in his eye. 'Quite an interesting little case, I think you'll find.'

'Thanks very much indeed,' I said eagerly.

'Right, off you go then.' He turned away. 'Now then, yes, sir. What can we do for you?'

I made my way from the room clutching my first brief like a baby to my bobbly Bulgarian chest.

I put the brief down on my desk and looked at it. What a splendid sight, so crisp and white with its thin pink sash. Yes, it certainly was a fine-looking brief. Nicely typed too in bold black official-looking letters. *Police* v. *Savage*. It was almost unimaginable that I should have a client, a real person depending for his defence on none other than . . . Well to say 'none other' was not quite accurate perhaps, as the names of both Mike Deacon and Jim Harbutt had at some stage been written and crossed out on the backsheet. Poor Mr Savage had been kicked around chambers a bit before bottoming out on my desk. My first client . . . I walked a few paces off and squinted down at the brief lying there. My own name shouted up at me from a blurred background of white, thrilling yet somehow not credible: they couldn't mean me. As I stood thinking what the brief represented in terms of responsibility, all the things I had learned as a student and as a pupil paled away as though the time had never been. I felt like an impostor.

I advanced on the thing again and picked it up. Solemnly, as though performing a ritual, I slipped off the tape and spread out the heavy cream sheets of the instructions. The first sentence which caught my eye had me rather puzzled.

'Unfortunately the true defence in this case cannot be put forward.'

I read:

'Namely, that if this defendant had in fact managed to get it up, the transfer of weight would have toppled him over.'

What had my client been trying to get up? I turned the page and all became clear. Mr Savage was charged with indecent exposure.

I was sitting there rather pink-faced when Jim came in looking for Freddy, who was visiting his wine merchant. Proudly I displayed my brief. Jim offered congratulations and wanted to know what kind of case it was. I handed him the instructions.

'Oh lord. A flasher? Has old Norman got a sense of humour after all?' He started to laugh. When he reached the comment about the transfer of weight he laughed louder. 'Who's been sending such . . . ribald instructions to a lady? Ah, I see, a return of Mike's. Only to be expected. One thing though, it says here, "the enclosed statement of the defendant". I don't see it here. Did they forget to enclose it?'

'Yes,' I said.

'A cock-up,' he said. 'Sorry, that might perhaps have been more delicately put. Never mind, you'll just have to play it by ear, that's all. No problem. Now, let's see, are you straight on the procedure? What do you call the bench?'

'Your worships?'

'Certainly not. Address the chairman or woman as sir or madam. You don't want to sound like a solicitor. What else? Let's see . . . Remember: if you decide to open for the defence, you don't get a closing speech; don't ask leading questions in chief; speak up clearly, don't mumble, and make sure you have a clean handkerchief before you go. I think that just about covers it. Now what about a drink? You'll be all right; I'm convinced of it.'

'Thanks,' I said, far from convinced myself.

'A flasher though, of all things . . . I didn't think old Norm had it in him.' He began laughing once more. 'I should say he wants his backside smacked.'

'Not by me,' I responded rather tartly. 'I've already got all the indelicacies I can handle for the moment.'

Everybody was very helpful. Mike Deacon showed me where to find the much-thumbed railway timetable in the clerks' room;

Graham lent me his new edition of *Stone's Justices' Manual* and said he didn't mind saying a flasher to start with was a bit too much of a good thing; David Jermaine bought me a large gin and provided a number of pieces of robust advice; even Bill Armstrong suggested some points for mitigation of sentence. I should have been gladder of this kindly support, however, without the riotous mirth which went with it. There seemed to be something in the idea of a female first-timer trying to defend a seventy-year-old flasher which struck these people as irresistibly comic. Even the Temple Comedian smiled.

'Start as you mean to go on, old girl, eh?' someone said, slapping me on the back.

Certainly not, I thought. I had come to the Bar aiming to become a person of distinction not some kind of knockabout comedian.

After a bad night's sleep broken every half hour or so by groping visits to the clock which I had placed out of reach on the windowsill – to check that the alarm was properly set – I got up at a quarter to six and made myself a cup of coffee. I felt dreadful; my head ached and my eyes were like live coals. Something in the kitchen was making dismal squeaking noises. I realized it was my stomach. Would eating improve matters? Absolutely not. Indeed, it seemed to me then that my situation would be improved by nothing short of immediate emigration to Australia. I was terrified. The coffee sank down and made dark and dyspeptic whirlpools in my innards; my stomach creaked. Heavily I got up, washed, dressed, put on my thick black coat, bundled my brief and *Stone's Manual* into my briefcase and let myself out of the flat. It was twenty past six in the morning.

Outside I started walking. My steps rang like iron on the cold pavement. In the light of a streetlamp frost crystals by the road's verge twinkled like quartz. I looked up at the flinty stars and shivered, changing my briefcase to the other hand; already *Stone* was beginning to live up to its name. My breath streamed before me as I puffed along. Passing a shop window I had a sudden clear view of myself in my black Bulgarian suit and greatcoat, rolling through the winter streets like a monstrous pinecone. The air had done nothing to revive me; I still felt terrible, only colder. And this was my first day as a real, working barrister. I wondered how I would like the rest.

* * *

The place had a Coketown atmosphere: heavily industrial but small and isolated, as though progress had seduced it then tossed it aside like a Victorian maiden. The courthouse was a squat old building made of red brick. Its architect, obviously prudent, had added a bulbous spire, perhaps feeling that if it fell short of the mark as a courthouse it might do as a church. It huddled halfway up a hill in the lee of a high railway bridge and had been built into the side of the slope in such a way that parts of it were extremely lofty and others low, as though it were standing on one leg. From the hill a drab blanket of river mist screened the town; here and there the red of a traffic light thinly pierced the grey. Suddenly out of the unknown an express train hurled itself with an infernal roar onto the bridge, screamed across and was gone. I wished I were aboard that train – anywhere but here.

I pushed through a pair of glass-topped swing doors and found myself in a tiled antehall in which there might have been twenty people waiting. A smell of old Woodbines and wet cardigans permeated the place. I stepped inside and inflated my lungs. I had now reached such a state of numb terror that it seemed that all my physical functions had stopped apart from the terrible pumping inside my ears. I had to keep remembering to breathe. I took a few steps forward on legs which felt like pipe-cleaners. First I must find my client. I cleared my throat.

'Er, is Mr Savage here, please?'

Nobody so much as turned a head in my direction. I realized I would have to do better than a hoarse whisper.

'Er, Mr Savage?' I called. This time it came out as a croak.

An elderly woman looked round. 'What did you say, duck?'

'Mr Savage! Mr Savage! Are you here, Mr Savage?' I bellowed, surprising myself and no doubt the assembled company by the furious volume of a hoot which would not have shamed a foghorn. Funnily enough I at once felt much better. To anyone paralysed by nervous shock, I would warmly recommend shouting one's head off.

'Are you all right, dear?' asked the woman in mild surprise.

I was drawing breath to let loose another scream when there was a reply: a small noise, really no more than a squeak. Turning, I saw sitting on a bench nearby a little old twig of a man wearing a very long raincoat, a muffler and, rather unexpectedly, a navy-blue beret of the kind generally associated with French onion-sellers.

He wore this not in the Gallic fashion but pulled tightly down over his ears, giving a dismal impression matched by the face beneath. He looked like a frightened peg-doll and so sad that I at once felt sorry for him. For the first time since yesterday, I realized, I was thinking of someone other than myself. Incredibly I had found someone who felt even worse than I did.

'Mr Savage?' I said. 'Good morning. I'm here to represent you today.'

The old man shot me a quick apprehensive glance. 'Er, I wasn't expecting a lady; I was looking for a Mr Harbutt,' he whispered; gazing hopefully over my shoulder in case Jim should jump out from behind and offer a trick or treat.

'I'm sorry to say that Mr Harbutt was engaged in another court. I've been asked to represent you instead.' I added, 'I hope you don't mind?' for the old man continued to fix me with eyes round with dread.

I was wondering whether he had realized I was an impostor, and if so how, when he suddenly said, 'I'm sure you've had a lot of experience of this sort of thing but it's a bit difficult talking to a lady about what's supposed to have happened.'

His voice trailed away unhappily. Here was an aspect I had not foreseen – so busy had I been thinking of it from the female point of view.

'Don't worry about that, Mr Savage,' I assured him earnestly. 'You've no idea how many cases like this I do in a week – no idea at all . . .' And lucky he hasn't, I thought. 'Oh yes, this kind of problem is always cropping up.' I went on in a sweeping manner from which it might have been thought that the south of England was one enormous nudist camp. The little old man eyed me nervously and said nothing.

'Well now, well now. Just tell me the facts as far as you can remember, Mr Savage; I'll jot them down in my notebook here and then we'll all know what's what, won't we?' I cried in the jolly tone of a nursery nurse. There was no reply.

'You know, Mr Savage, you'll have to tell me whatever you can if I'm to represent you properly. You really must try and say something.'

The old chap shrunk into himself like a sea polyp, with which in the field of communication he seemed to have much in common. I felt somewhat at a loss.

'Perhaps we should wait for Mr Morgan to come from the solicitors then?' I suggested after a minute or two.

The old man nodded. 'I think that would be best.'

I would have liked to pace about and appear busy as I had seen others doing outside court but, doubtful about my pipecleaner legs, I instead sat down glumly beside my client on the bench. There was a silence broken only by the occasional wheezy sigh from Mr Savage. It was very depressing.

We must have been sitting there side by side for about five minutes although it seemed longer, when the solicitor's representative finally arrived. A fresh problem presented itself. This was not Mr Morgan; it was a girl – inoffensive-looking, bespectacled and small; but a female nonetheless. Mr Savage's eyes widened in dismay, as I am sure did my own.

'Er, I wasn't expecting a lady. I was hoping Mr Morgan would be coming. Isn't he coming?' His voice held a note of panic.

'I'm afraid Mr Morgan's out of the office this morning,' said the girl. 'Things are all a bit up in the air with him today actually.' She giggled and stared out of the window vaguely as though half-expecting the errant Morgan to come soaring past. 'They've sent me instead, with the file,' she said.

Mr Savage looked from one to the other of us like a cornered rabbit. I could almost see him considering whether to make a bolt for it through the swing doors. There was an awkward pause. It occurred to me after a time that, as the senior person, I was expected to give a lead if we were not to sit there like a row of cornstooks for the rest of the morning.

'Um, Mr Savage, I suppose you wouldn't like the case postponed?' I suggested hopefully.

My poor old client trembled. 'Oh, no. I couldn't. I'm under the hospital with me nerves as it is. Came and had it put off once before. Drive me potty, that would.'

I turned to the girl. 'Do you think, Miss er . . .'

'Daff.' 'Do you think, Miss er . . . Daff, that you could give me any idea of what the case is about?'

Daff considered this plea in silence. 'I reely don't think so, sorry,' she said. 'I wouldn't like to be sure.'

The thought of being sure about anything seemed at this moment an unbelievable luxury.

'You wouldn't have a copy of the summons on file by any

chance?' I asked her. 'That might have the facts written on it, you know.'

'I wouldn't know about that,' said the girl.

'Er, there was a statement referred to in the instructions but unfortunately none was enclosed. You wouldn't have a copy in the file, I suppose?'

Daff thought. 'Do you want me to look?'

'That's a very good idea,' I said, as she put the file down on the bench and began poring over the three or four short letters it contained.

'What would it look like, do you know? There doesn't seem . . . It's all a bit out of date. Sorry.'

'Never mind,' I said.

'You see,' Daff explained, 'I don't know the ins and outs of the case. I'm just here with the file.'

'Well, thanks very much,' I said, wondering if Daff wasn't cargo our frail ship might get on faster without. 'But if you've things to be getting on with in the office, please don't let me keep you.'

The girl goggled at this piece of ignorance. 'Oh, I'm supposed to stay and sit behind you all the time,' she said. 'In case you need any assistance during the case.'

I turned to my client. It was hard to suppress a feeling of faint desperation.

'I know this won't be very easy, but could you perhaps try to think of me as a doctor?' I suggested.

'I went to fetch me pants hanging on the line,' said Mr Savage, charging without warning into the breach. 'I'd washed them the night before. I had me mac on,' he added. ''Cause it was raining.'

'Yes?' I said, when it seemed that he had finished.

Reluctantly, Mr Savage went into forward gear once more. 'When I got to the line the pants were gone. I thought they must have blown down the road. I'd just set off after them when these two old ladies started swearing and shouting at me. I tried to tell them I was only looking for me pants but they just kept hitting me over the head. Vicious, they were. The policeman came only just in time.' He shook his head, lips pursed. 'I know now how those pop idols must feel,' he remarked.

'The prosecution is alleging that you exposed your, er, private parts to these ladies?' I said rather hesitantly.

'I don't know about that.'

'How do you mean? That is, why don't you know?'

'It must have been the wind.'

'I beg your pardon?'

'It must have got up me mac.'

'Er, why weren't you wearing anything in fact?' To be asking so many impertinent questions felt very odd.

'I was wearing me mac, wasn't I?'

'Yes, but underneath?'

'Well, you see, I'd lost me pants . . .'

I was considering a new line of questioning when he went on, 'Got no 'umanity, some people haven't. When I looked at meself I was black and blue all over; a right mass of weals . . .'

'Yes, well that sounds satisfactory,' I said, 'Oh, sorry, I meant your account of the matter.' I added hastily, noticing that Mr Savage appeared rather offended. 'Now then, quite obviously the next thing to be done is . . .'

What was the next thing to be done? Think . . . Ah, find the officer in the case? That was what other members of chambers always did.

' . . . Yes, as I say, the obvious thing now is to find the prosecuting officer, so if you'll just wait here a moment, Mr Savage, I'll um . . . Oh, good morning, officer. Yes, this is Mr Savage. Er, yes. Just stay there a moment, Mr Savage, would you, and I'll . . .'

Taking the helm in this manner, I went a little way down the corridor to go through the procedure of finding out from the officer, a comfortable-looking middle-aged constable, the nature of the case against my client. Mr Savage, he said, was alleged to have come through his garden gate wearing only a mackintosh and to have put all he had on display to a pair of old ladies who had taken it amiss.

The 'lady allegators', said the policeman, had then chased the defendant into a public park, and had been attempting to carry out a citizens' arrest by hooking him round the ankles with their umbrellas near the cricket pavilion when he succeeded in finding a police officer and giving himself up. Although badly winded, he had managed to puff out a confession, begging to be taken into protective custody. He had then been driven to the hospital and treated for shock. I could not help thinking that, even if my poor old client had been guilty of this offence, he had already paid for it many times over.

Mr Savage was sitting where I had left him, looking more like a sad peg-doll than ever. I would have liked to ask him why he wore a beret pulled down in that uncomfortable manner, or indeed why he wore one at all, but I had asked him enough personal questions for one morning. As I approached, he paled visibly, his lips trembled and I could see his knees shaking under his mackintosh. Whatever could be the matter now? Before my eyes my client was turning to jelly. I became aware then that it was not myself but something further down the hallway that was responsible for the mischief.

One was tall and one small. The tall one had beady eyes and a tufted wart at the end of a nose like a lobster-claw. The small one was fat with the face of an angry currant bun. These must be the lady allegators. I could almost hear the clop of jaws as black-coated, hatted, booted and armed with umbrellas the two marched shoulder to shoulder across the hall and disappeared through a door at the end. I found it unimaginable that my meek client should have wanted to show those two anything but a fast-retreating back. I was trying to think whether this argument could be used to advantage when an urgent whisper came from an unexpected direction.

'I'll plead guilty.'

'What's that? Mr Savage? Where are you? What are you doing under the table?'

'Never mind about that. Have those two gone? I'll admit it all; put me hands up to the lot. Just don't let those two get at me. Drive me potty, this will . . .'

'Look,' I said, worried that the strain might indeed have done just that. 'You can't plead guilty to something you didn't do just because you're frightened of two old ladies. Do come out, Mr Savage. I can't talk to you down there. Don't worry, I'll protect you.'

For some reason this seemed to reassure him, for shortly afterwards the navy-blue tortoise head reappeared from below followed by the rest of his thin body.

Thinking to take his mind off his immediate worries, I suggested we go into court. 'After all, they'll hardly try to have a go at you in front of the magistrates,' I said. 'Think what a bad impression it would give.'

My client shook his head in a depressed manner but allowed himself to be led into court without protest.

The courtroom was roughly the shape of a wedge of cheese. The well was in the low-ceilinged part and the height of the chamber gradually rose to an imposing grandeur with the bench somewhere near the top. I looked up. Surely it couldn't be? It was. Side by side, sharp and beady as before, were sitting the two women we had seen in the hall: not the allegators, but the magistrates.

'They're there again, same as last week,' whispered Mr Savage. Ladies everywhere. Drive me potty, this will.' He subsided trembling into the back row, got out a handkerchief and blew his nose with a sound like the last trump. I had to admit that poor Mr Savage had had a run of extraordinarily bad luck.

I bowed to the bench and took a seat in counsel's row. After all we had been through, the morning had been very long and I was surprised to find that the business of the day was only just beginning. As I sat down the clerk to the magistrates rose from his desk, stepped back a few paces, cupped his hands round his mouth and shouted up in a respectful manner at the bench, 'May it please you, madam, to constitute yourselves licensing justices?'

'Very good, Mr Whitworth. This is now a licensing bench.'

'Madam, the case of Singh on your licensing list has been adjourned and is now fixed for next Monday week.'

'Very good, Mr Whitworth.'

'Madam, that concludes the business of the licensing court. May it please you now, madam, to constitute yourselves examining magistrates?'

'Yes, Mr Whitworth, we are now examining magistrates.'

'Thank you, madam. I understand the officer in the case of Batt to be seeking a remand.'

A heavy-set sergeant had appeared in the witness-box. 'Yes, madam, this is to be a new-style committal and I would ask for a week's remand in order to pursue further inquiries.'

'Do the police oppose a renewal of bail?'

'No, madam.'

'So be it. Remanded one week; bail extended on same terms.'

'Madam,' trumpeted the clerk, 'would you now constitute yourselves justices of the peace for the purpose of hearing overnight charges?'

'Yes, Mr Whitworth, we are now justices of the peace . . .'

After all these changes of form accomplished in such a short time without any sign of effort on the part of the two ladies, I would not have been surprised to see them constitute themselves vampire bats and fly through the window. Indeed, it would have been a welcome diversion. At the thought of the approaching trial my knees had turned to wire and fuzz once more and my wits to something similar.

'Case of *Police* against *Savage*.'

And then to my terror it began: my first venture into advocacy. Blood congealed to mercury; heart bursting to squeeze it through channels contracted needle-thin with fear. I poured a glass of water from the carafe at my elbow. It rattled against the glass and the glass against my teeth as I gulped down a mouthful tasting of dust. The prosecuting officer galloped in and out of his opening as if playing a private game of beat-the-clock and hustled up the first real allegator, an old-fashioned rose of an elderly lady who gave her evidence with unshakeable conviction, positively identified Mr Savage as the offender and generally did as much damage as the prosecution could have hoped. The policeman sat down and it was my turn to cross-examine.

Suddenly I was on my feet. It was like stepping onto a stage; with a sense of total unreality and detachment, I waited to hear if words would come and what they would turn out to be.

'Now then, Miss Beale,' said a voice, calm and measured and quite unidentifiable as mine. 'If you wear glasses, did you have them on at the time you saw, or to be accurate say you saw, what you, er, say you saw?'

'I beg your pardon?'

'At the time you have told us about, when you say you saw, well anyway, at that time, did you have glasses on?'

'No.'

'Do you wear glasses?'

'No. My vision fortunately is extremely keen.'

'You don't believe it possible that what you, er, thought you saw could have in fact been the end of Mr Savage's belt, for example?'

'I should say,' remarked the old lady mildly, 'that if I had been unable to tell a belt from a gentleman's . . . parts, I should have found myself in some strange situations before now.'

Perhaps I could trap the old lady with a practical test, as they were always doing on the television.

'Now then, madam,' I said to the witness. 'Perhaps you would be so kind as to demonstrate your powers to the court by reading the title of this book from where you are standing.' I held up *Stone's Justices' Manual*.

'Certainly. It says *Stone's Justices' Manual*.'

'Aha,' I said, hoping to sidestep this unhelpful answer by Jim Harbutt's rhetorical methods. 'So that's what you say, is it?'

'Well, is it or is it not, Miss Hunter?' said the woman with the hook nose in a peppery manner. 'It's all very well waving your books about but it's no good to us up here, you know. Is that what it says or isn't it? Very well. A moment please. I am writing that down. "Witness demonstrates ability to read book title at distance of twenty feet." Very well.'

'Now then, I don't believe you have told the court how far you were away from my client at the time when you say you saw, er, what you saw or say you saw?'

'I'm sorry, could you repeat that?' said the old lady.

'How far . . .'

'Oh. About five feet, I should have said, or perhaps less.'

The next lady witness was the sister of the first; still a moss rose, but larger and more prickly. Bearing in mind the golden rule of cross-examination – never ask a question to which you do not know the answer – I was more careful and, although the questions I could ask were few, I managed, without doing much good, at least to do no harm. I had almost begun to hope that I might have laid the foundations for an inkling of doubt when my evil genius prompted me to say, as I was about to conclude, 'Oh, by the way, when you say you saw what you say it was you saw, did you say anything?'

'Yes, I did,' replied the old lady. 'I said to him, "You can put that away, my lad. I've not been a district nurse for twenty-nine years without seeing more of those than you've had hot dinners."'

I sat down for the second time that day more quickly than I had got up.

Still, I was not downhearted, a fact which I can now only attribute to youth and inexperience. There remained the police officer; we weren't done yet.

'Now, officer, the weather. Blustery, rainy, was it?'

The policeman said he particularly remembered the day because a colleague had suffered heatstroke.

'Well then, hot and blustery, was it?' I was ready to compromise.

'No wind, madam.'

'The odd thundery shower perhaps?' Freak storms, bursts of
hail, I was ready to try anything; rising damp . . .

'It was a fine hot day, madam.'

'Well, in any case I must put it to you that it was raining.'

It was uphill work and it seemed a long time until I came to the
end. 'Officer, you've told us Mr Savage confessed. What do you
say were his precise words?'

The witness consulted his notebook. 'He said, "It's a right
bloomer. I've blown it this time."'

'Officer,' I responded with sudden inspiration, 'can you be
certain that he did not in fact say, "It's my white bloomers.
They've blown off the line?" Think before you answer now.'

'No need to think, madam. I'd say it was impossible.'

'How can you be so sure?'

'Well, in the first place I was there and heard him, madam. In
the second place, I've known men to confess to just about every
crime in the calendar, but I don't believe there is a man, even your
client, madam, who'd admit to owning a pair of white
bloomers . . .'

'Mr Savage, you have been found guilty of the offence as
charged,' said the bun-faced chairlady not unkindly. 'And we feel
that a probation order may be appropriate in your case. Is there a
probation officer in court? Will three weeks be a sufficient
adjournment for the preparation of a report?'

'Quite sufficient, thank you, madam,' said the probation officer, a young girl with long black hair. 'I shall have no problem . . .'

Just you wait and see, I thought.

'. . . Drive me potty this will.' It was as though Mr Savage had
spoken aloud.

Poor soul, it seemed that, far from being over, his trials were
just beginning.

I did not say goodbye to Mr Savage in the end. It didn't seem
appropriate somehow. I went away and left him there on a bench
in the entrance hall, sobbing in the arms of a huge police sergeant.

12

Outside the window wet grey snow was falling. Great flakes flopped onto the sill and dissolved into grimy tears on the pane. Bleakly I gazed down into the street at hatted heads muffled and bent, bobbing along the dark pavement; at cars hooded with sleet crawling like aphids in the road. It was a foul morning with the promise of worse to come. January should be abolished, I thought, struck from the calendar as a matter of public policy.

Turning away, I peered along the dim catacomb of passages towards the entrance doors and was relieved to see that nobody was coming. It was five to eleven. Perhaps my case would not be heard today after all. Could someone have made a mistake? Despite the warmth of the radiator I was cold. It must be nerves. My feet had become strangers and my stomach an echoing cave full of small bats. I slid my hands mandarin-fashion into the sleeves of my gown to warm my fingers. Here I was without a brief, which would have been nasty enough in a criminal case at the magistrates' court. Here in the county court, however, with a civil case on my hands, I ran the risk of having to grapple with sudden points of law.

In addition to worry I was bedevilled by a sense of injustice. My plans for today had been quite different: in a word, truancy. Nothing spectacular; a stroll down Oxford Street perhaps, a quick glance round the shops, where I might just fall prey to the temptation of a new dress for next Saturday's party. I had not envisaged being huddled here in this corridor like a sentenced criminal waiting for the public stocks to open for business.

Less than an hour ago I had been cheerful, lighthearted, a woman with hardly a care in the world. Sailing down the escalator towards the eastbound tube on my way to chambers, I rehearsed what I would say to Norman: 'Morning, Norman,' I would call out casually. 'As Mr Tobin's not in today, I'm stepping out for a haircut . . .' That didn't sound too frivolous, did it? Ah, it was a grand thing to be self-employed, to be your own master.

As I came up the steps at Temple station, the first fat snow flakes were being whipped up into flurries by the wind from the river. There was an exhilarating sense of winter and I laughed as one flake settled on the end of my nose. In this mood of pleasant idiocy I loitered across the road and in at the gates. In the square I caught sight of the carpark attendant, a glum Führer figure generally to be seen with a damp sponge in hand enjoying his favourite sport, gumming 'no parking' notices on windscreens. Not today, it seemed. Standing there motionless in his dark livery, he resembled a figure in a snowstorm globe shaken by a child. I wondered if his sponge had frozen.

I put my head around the clerks' room door into a solid wall of heat.

'Morning, Jackie; morning, Paul; morning, Norman,' I called out casually. 'Just stepping out for a –'

'Miss Hunter, where have you been?' The words were full of veiled possibilities, none of them pleasant.

'Miss Hunter, could you come back in here a moment, please? Oh, there you are. I was saying, where have you been? Paul here's been trying to contact you for the past half-hour.'

'I'm sorry,' I said with intense unease. 'Why? There's nothing the matter, is there?'

'You're in court this morning, that's what's the matter. Look at the time, nearly twenty past ten. It won't do, Miss Hunter, coming in as late as this, you know. Do you realize, I was about to return your brief out of chambers?' He spoke with such horror of the possibility of having to hand my brief on to another set of chambers, that I was ashamed of my instant reaction: a stab of fierce regret that I had not arrived later.

'Where's the brief?' I asked in a strangled tone.

'Oh, there's no brief as such. You'll pick it up as you go along,' Norman said with a glib confidence which seemed to me to be in poor taste. 'First on at 10.30. Westminster County Court. Something for the legal advice centre. Been overlooked. I've no idea what it is; the centre didn't know much. Client will explain at court, or try to. Name's Mackenzie. That's all I can tell you.'

'Well, thanks, Norman.' If he noticed the sarcasm, he ignored it.

'Not at all. Well, Miss Hunter, you'd best get going,' he remarked with all the complacency of someone who was going nowhere himself. 'I'd get a taxi if I were you.' He looked at the clock above the door. 'Lucky the court's not far. You should make it by twenty-five-to if you step on it. Don't forget your robes. Hey, Paul, what's happened to that coffee?' I withdrew into the corridor.

'Oh, by the way, Miss Hunter,' he called after me. 'It's quite a heavy claim, I understand. They've set the whole day aside for the hearing.'

In the circumstances that was all I needed.

Within minutes I found myself gasping for breath like a landed trout as I rocketed up the Strand in the back of a taxi towards St Martin's Lane. I lit a cigarette with trembling hands. It tasted vile but I drew in the smoke violently. I was full of irritable self-pity. What sort of a rotten job was this, anyway, which put you at everybody's beck and call? That legal advice centre seemed to think that they had only to pick up the phone whenever something had been 'overlooked' and someone like me would be glad to drop everything and come and grapple with a tangle of loose ends for a fee which might just about cover the taxi fare. The case would very likely be a shambles. When I got to court my client would probably be there with six relatives all talking at once and nobody with the least idea of what the case was about. If there was a point of law involved, heaven forfend, I would have to borrow books from the judge's private room and look it up in the corridor while everyone waited for me. At this horrible thought, despite the cold I could feel myself beginning to prickle with sweat. Could I apply to have the case adjourned on the grounds that I had had no time to take proper instructions? Impossible: the whole day had been set aside for the case.

I took a deep breath. It was no good panicking. Whatever happened, I must try to appear calm and confident, for I knew that any display of doubt or inexperience on my part would have the same effect on the client as an announcement by a surgeon that he had not done many operations and hoped the patient would excuse the odd slip of the knife.

The weather was growing worse. The taxi had slowed to a

crawl, wipers batting furiously against a vortex of whirling white. I glanced at my watch. Twenty-five to eleven already. My imagination conjured up a vision of the judge, my opponent, the client and twenty or so irritable witnesses pacing around waiting for me. To distract my attention, I considered the case, which was only marginally less awful. Norman had said it was quite a heavy claim. How heavy? Could as much as fifty pounds be at stake, a hundred even? What sort of a case was it? Landlord and tenant? A motoring claim? Hire purchase perhaps? Provided it isn't hire purchase or a credit sale agreement, I bargained with providence, I won't complain.

I was surprised to find the court building completely deserted. Alone in the robing room, I put on my wig, gown and bands, and taking my notebook went out into the corridor to wait. The snow was still falling fast. Everybody must have been delayed. There was no sign of life – just yards and yards of passageways, all painted a dull vegetable green, heavily pipelined and empty.

After a while I looked at my watch. Nearly a quarter past eleven. My spirits began to lift a little. I wondered how soon I could decently leave. It seemed clear that no one was coming.

My thoughts were cut short at this point by the appearance of what could only be my client. He was over six feet in height and broad to match. The lower part of his meaty trunk had been squeezed into a pair of trews made of the brightest tartans I had ever seen. Over a tea-cosy sweater in bumblebee stripes he wore a see-through plastic mackintosh several sizes too small, and this lively costume was topped with a knitted bobble-cap in baby blue. His face was black and very amiable and as I came to introduce myself he gave me a broad smile, revealing teeth of such whiteness and regularity that I was reminded of a grand piano.

'Mr Mackenzie?' I said. 'My name's Hunter and I am here to represent you this morning.'

'That's fine, ma'am.' Mr Mackenzie extricated from the mac an arm the size of a leg of lamb and we formally shook hands. 'The gentleman at the centre said I should give you these, ma'am,' he said and began patting himself here and there, producing a collection of dog-eared papers piecemeal from this pocket and that while I watched, half expecting a rabbit to appear.

Eventually he had a sheaf which he handed to me, and then began divesting himself of his dripping outer clothes, folding up each item small before placing it carefully on top of the radiator. I wondered if the mac would melt, then deciding that it was no business of mine, began sorting through the papers.

At first sight these were not very helpful. There was a letter from a relative in Jamaica, which I handed back; there were two or three receipted bills and a letter from the Gas Board threatening to cut off his supply. Finally I came upon my brief: a flimsy sheet of pink paper from the legal advice centre, faintly typed as follows:

TO WHOM IT MAY CONCERN

This client has started his own action for personal injuries. He wishes representation for the hearing and has paid 3 guineas.

AG

I made up my mind that I would find out who AG was and make the rest of his life a misery if I could.

'Well, Mr Mackenzie,' I said opening my notebook. 'I think we'd better start right from the beginning, don't you?'

The facts of the case were simple enough. Mr Mackenzie had been employed by a large hotel in Mayfair as a kitchen porter. One evening while carrying a dustbin at work he had fallen and been injured. He had started an action for damages, claiming that his employers were to blame for the accident. Yesterday at the last moment he had decided that he would like a barrister to represent him in court and had gone to the legal advice centre to hire one. He was sorry to say that on the way here he must have dropped his particulars of claim and all the other court documents in the snow.

I tried to picture my examination notes on the subject of a master's duty to his servant and was relieved to find that my recollection seemed fairly sound. Had the National Metropolitan Hotel failed to take reasonable care for Mr Mackenzie's safety: that was what it all boiled down to. And what were the categories of reasonable care? Safe fellow-servants, that was the first. It seemed a long shot but I would be methodical.

'Mr, Mackenzie,' I said, 'could any of the other hotel staff be said to have been er, unsafe, do you think? I mean, in any way which might have had a bearing on the accident?'

My client's tufty eyebrows rose. 'Unsafe, ma'am?'

'Well, I don't know: practical jokes, fits of rage, that kind of thing?'

Mr Mackenzie shook his head regretfully. 'The cook was unsafe, no doubt about that, but he was off sick the night I have me accident.'

'Right, we'll leave that then.'

I thought again. There was always the duty to provide safe equipment.

'Er, was there anything wrong with the dustbin as far as you could see?'

Again my client shook his head. As far as he could remember, it had been an ordinary metal dustbin with nothing unusual about it.

'Could you tell me something about your system of work, Mr Mackenzie?'

My client wrinkled his brows in puzzlement. 'System of work, ma'am?'

'I mean, how did you actually go about your work? What did the work consist of?'

'Well,' he said carefully after some consideration. 'First I pick up the bin in the kitchen and then I carry she outside.'

'Yes?' I said encouragingly, but with this graphic description of the scope of his employment Mr Mackenzie seemed to have shot his bolt. 'Did you have to carry it far?' I probed.

'Down the passage, about here to there,' my client waved an arm rather vaguely. 'And then up them slip'ry slimy stairs . . .'

'Did you say, slippery slimy stairs?'

'Yes. Up them slip'ry slimy stairs where I lose me foot in the accident.'

'I see, what you're saying is, you lost your footing on those stairs?'

'That's right. There me tumble over, ma'am.'

Suddenly I could see it; our case against the National Metropolitan Hotel. My excitement surprised me; I had never been on a winner before: and this one was a winner, I was sure of it; a classic case of an employer's neglect to provide a safe place of work. Because of a belief in his rights, this simple, uneducated man was ready to pit himself against the might of a large organization. I supposed that, even without the cheap legal representation provided by the centre, he would have been prepared to go in and fight his own case. One could hardly fail to admire such spirit, and to see him get what he deserved would be a heartwarming experience.

'How often were the stairs cleaned?' I asked.

Mr Mackenzie shook his head and said that as far as he could remember they had never been cleaned at all.

'Then what sort of condition were they in at the time of the accident?'

He pursed his lips in disgust. 'Them steps was a real disgrace. Covered with papers and I don't know what. And dangerous. Them steps been real slip'ry slimy since I been there. A lot of people fell. Yes, ma'am, a real disgrace.'

I wondered if the management had been aware of the situation. 'Mr Mackenzie, do you know whether anyone complained about the state of the stairs?'

'Complained? I should say so. Why, every time anybody tumble down you should have heard the language –'

'Actually, what I meant was, did anybody complain to the management? Were the stairs ever inspected?'

Mr Mackenzie thought not.

As my confidence in our case increased, I began to look about for our opponents. It seemed that Mr Mackenzie and I were still the only people in the building and it occurred to me that perhaps the defendants might not be coming at all. Could I believe my luck? Had they decided to let the case go undefended? I would go and find out from the judge's clerk whether or not a defence had been filed. Perhaps we would have a walkover.

I almost collided in the doorway with an awesome party. First came a robed barrister of striking polish and seniority, about whom pupils and solicitors' clerks bobbed and nosed like tugboats round a liner. In his wake sailed two influential-looking men: foreign city bankers, perhaps; one in a shaggy fur coat and the other in velvet-trimmed cashmere.

I turned smartly around and dodged back to my client. 'Have you seen any of those people before?' I asked under my breath.

'Oh yes, ma'am,' my client hissed back in a delighted stage whisper. 'The one with the long nose, he's the hotel manager; and the one in the mink coat's the head waiter. Fancy them coming here for me case. I've got that hotel really worried, it's plain to see.' Mr Mackenzie was enjoying himself. 'Oh look, ma'am, there's the general manager coming in now.' He chuckled. 'We going to take that hotel for a walk today, ma'am, no doubt about that.'

I had been wrong. The other side were defending, and defending

in some style by the look of it. The suspicion that there might be
more to this case than met the eye nagged at my mind. I thrust it
aside, but one question could not be fudged: what were all these
distinguished personages doing here in a case of otherwise so
little significance?

Ah, but it wasn't of little significance. Suddenly I recalled
Norman's parting words: a heavy claim. Until now I had overlooked that aspect completely. I had not even asked Mr
Mackenzie what injuries he had suffered. Although he had now
apparently recovered, the poor man had obviously been badly
hurt.

'Mr Mackenzie,' I said. 'What injuries did you receive in the
accident?'

Mr Mackenzie smiled and shook his head. 'No, ma'am,' he said,
rolling his eyes heavenward. 'Thanks be to Gad, I wasn't
scratched myself.'

'But if you weren't injured at all, what are we here for?'

'Why, ma'am to fight they of course.' My client pointed a
bellicose finger towards the gathering crowd of fur coats in the
opposite corner.

'But, excuse me, what are we supposed to be fighting about?'

'Damage to me denture, of course,' said Mr Mackenzie.

I could hardly believe my ears. Inexperience and unimportant I
might have been, but even I had never envisaged coming to court
to fight about a pair of National Health false teeth.

'That's the whole pint, ma'am. I may have forgot to mention it.
When me lose me foot the denture fly out of me jaw, into the air,
fall in the bin and get broke. It cost me seven pound to get she
mended. I got the bill somewhere.'

'So we're fighting about seven pounds?' Mr Mackenzie and his
case were beginning to prey on my nerves.

'No, ma'am, you don't understand. The seven pound is only for
damage to me denture. I'm claiming a thousand pounds.'

'You're quite right,' I said, digesting this. 'I don't understand. If
you only suffered seven pounds' worth of damage, do you mind
telling me what on earth you're claiming a thousand pounds for?'

'It's the law,' my client said.

'Is that so?'

Yes. You see, when I was starting me case I read a book all
about the law.'

'Really, and what did it say?'

'It say . . .' Mr Mackenzie threw back his head, appearing to quote from memory. '"The maximum limit for a claim in the county court is one thousand pounds." So there didn't seem no sense in claiming less.'

At this point I fell into the grip of unreality. I could remember once having read a story of a man who went to bed in a four-poster, the canopy of which sank down gradually in the night and smothered him to death. I was beginning to think I knew how that man must have felt.

One thing was clear: to fight a heavy action about repairs to a set of dentures was ludicrous. There seemed to me one way of saving the situation: I would have to meet my opponent and brazen it out. He was probably as much in the dark as I had been about the real nature of Mr Mackenzie's damage. Suppose I were to approach him and ask what offer the hotel was prepared to make to settle the case? Perhaps the defendants might conjure up a figure which would enable us to leave with a certain amount of dignity. I glanced across the hall at my opponent and his satellites and quailed inwardly at the prospect of trying to bargain from such a weak position. I looked back at Mr Mackenzie, so full of confident anticipation, and was conscious of a strange feeling of unity with him, as though the two of us were ranged together against some large and unfathomable enemy. I must do the best I could for this poor man.

'Mr Mackenzie,' I said, 'I have no doubt now that our only hope is to try to settle this case for the best figure we can get.'

'Not fight? What are you saying, lady?'

I had admired Mr Mackenzie's spirit but I had not until now begun to comprehend what stuff this man was made of. My arguments in favour of a settlement were forceful – strengthened, I must admit, by fears of what the judge would do to me on discovering the basis of our claim for a thousand pounds. My own determination to settle, however, was more than matched by my client's resolution to fight. Mr Mackenzie simply brushed every argument aside with the reassuring comment: 'You're a clever lady, ma'am. You bound to think of something.'

This discussion was still proceeding when I realized that the usher had appeared and was conducting my opponent into court.

'The Lard,' said my client, changing tack, 'will give me what I deserve this day.' He raised his eyes piously to the piped green ceiling.

I did not share this confidence. From the way the day had been going, a thunderbolt seemed too much to hope for.

We moved towards the courtroom. Out of the corner of my eye I could see the usher in his black gown hovering outside the judge's door like a keeper about to set loose some exotic and unpredictable beast. We were about to pass over the threshold into court when a last thought struck me.

'Mr Mackenzie, just tell me who it was that was supposed to clean the stairs?'

'I may have forgot to mention, ma'am, that was me own job.'

I gaped at him, paralysed.

'You looking a bit pale, ma'am,' said my client. 'You feeling OK?'

I opened my mouth to speak but only a croak came out.

'I know what it is, ma'am, you a bit worried.' Mr Mackenzie showed only partial insight into the state of imbecile quaking terror into which I had fallen. 'I know what it is, you're frightened because you're only a woman and they in there is all men, but never you mind about that.' He raised one leg-o'-mutton arm protectively. 'You see, ma'am, I'll be with you . . .'

The rest of the proceedings were too terrible to describe. Mr Mackenzie not only lost his claim but was ordered to pay the costs of the defence, a sum it would probably take him years to earn. It could have gone no other way, but I was unhappy just the same. Despite the gallant manner in which he shook my hand outside the courtroom and his brilliant farewell smile, I could tell that his faith in British justice had been shaken. He would never quite understand what had gone wrong – and that was the saddest thing of all. I watched him wandering away down the passage in his bright sweater and bobble cap, wishing that I could have done better; feeling, illogically perhaps, that I or British justice had let him down.

'Never mind, ma'am, you done your best.'

Well, maybe.

Mr Mackenzie was right about one thing though.

In a strange way he is still with me.

13

A noise like a fire-engine tore through my sleep. Electrified by the terrible din, I shot upright, striking my head sharply as usual on the overhanging corner of the chest of drawers. Now keenly awake, I struggled out of bed. In the sudden silence I could just hear a faint ticking sound. Somewhere in the darkness my great brass alarm clock was mustering its strength to let loose another blast. Where had I hidden it the night before? In the wardrobe? No, not twice running. Under the bed? Too easy to find. I had outwitted myself. Quickly I began hunting round the small room but I was too late. The silence was ruptured by a second explosion of noise, intensified by the reverberations of the metal wastebin in which the clock sat. I silenced the brass beast and looked at it. 5.00 a.m. I sat down on the bed, shivering.

After a strong cup of coffee in the kitchen I was able to remember where I had left my briefcase the evening before. Why had I put it in the bathroom? Quietly I made my way back down the passage. All around me the flat lay soundless and still. This was the best time of the day, when the mind was at its most elastic, ready to map out grand designs, and so on. Famous people were always saying so in interviews. I snapped on the sitting-room light. All over London at this moment little lights must be beaming out across the darkness as famous people shook off sleep to keep this vigil with me. It was an inspiring thought. Here we all were stealing an intellectual march on the rest of the world. I yawned.

Reaching into my briefcase I brought out half a dozen eggs and put them on the table. Further research yielded a floppy packet of bacon and a paper bag of mushrooms rather squashed. That explained where my supper had gone – although not why I had put it in the bathroom. I found my brief and looked at it through eyes gritty with fatigue. *Police* v. *Pennyweather*: a motoring case at Epsom Magistrates' Court, defending for Messrs Wisely & Wisely.

I glanced at the brief fee on the backsheet. Seven guineas: that

meant a contested case; five for the brief, two for the conference.
Wiseley's standard rate was seven guineas altogether for a fight,
five for a guilty plea, and two if the case was adjourned to another
day. Although their fees were no better than average, Wiseley's
were quick payers; I might have to wait no more than six or nine
months before the hand dipped into the solicitorial pocket.

Wiseley's representative at court was normally Mr Kenworth, a
retired prison officer employed as Chief Managing Litigation Clerk
in their Motoring Department. Nor did this impressive title by any
means represent the full scope of Mr Kenworth's activities. Only a
week before 'the Chief Administrative Litigation Clerk of our
Licensing Department who will attend counsel at court' had
turned out to be Mr Kenworth, and he had also recently appeared as
'the Chief Managing Litigation Clerk of our Family Law Division'.
Altogether, Mr Kenworth was an important personage who might
justly have claimed to be the life and soul of the firm.

Not that he was exactly a lively figure in himself. A tall
lumbering man in his seventies, hugely solid and dressed
throughout the year in a droopy black overcoat, he resembled a
great bloodhound in a bowler hat. He seemed very much attached
to the hat – so much so that, although he would sometimes raise
it for reasons of courtesy or to mop beneath it in summer, I never
saw him actually take it off. He always carried a black briefcase
similar in shape to an old-fashioned doctor's bag, and in the other
hand a neatly furled umbrella, also black and so exceptionally fat
that I used to wonder what it would look like if he put it up.
Unfortunately he never did so, and on wet days the rain would
drip from the brim of his bowler in such a depressing manner that
I felt sorry for him. When he spoke, which was rarely, it was in an
oddly soft and piping voice like a piccolo note coming out of a
bassoon. I would have given a great deal to know what they had
made of Mr Kenworth in the prison service.

As an instructing solicitor he was ideal; instead of getting
anxious and upset, running round after witnesses, or asking unsettling questions about the powers of the magistrates or which
way the court was likely to jump, Mr Kenworth would select the
warmest corner, quietly make his way there and lean himself
against the wall until the time came to go into court, thus lending
support without interference. I also approved of his attitude
towards the results, which was that, however dreadful, they could

always have been a little worse. In the light of some of my own results, it was no wonder I found this a comfort. If I had been told that there were clients who found this phlegmatic philosophy exasperating, I would not have believed it.

I rubbed my eyes and spread the brief and its contents on the table. Mr Kenworth's happy-go-lucky philosophy was unfortunately also reflected in his instructions to counsel:

'Counsel is instructed to represent the defendant Alfred Pennyweather. The facts of the matter will appear from the enclosed summons. Suffice it to say . . .'

Suffice it to say, indeed. In the same way as such an expression as 'Well, very frankly' generally introduces a piece of woolly evasion, so 'Suffice it to say' in solicitors' instructions generally follows some vital omission. I found the summons, which luckily he had remembered to enclose, and read the following:

'At 8.00 a.m. on Monday, 18 April 1969, you were the driver of a Hillman saloon motor car Reg. No. XVS 224 travelling on the B280 road in an easterly direction towards its junction with the A24 road when having failed to observe the traffic signs or to accord precedence to northbound traffic the rear nearside of your vehicle was in collision at a point 45' south of the junction of that road with the A241 road with the front offside of a Triumph motor car Reg. No. PPY 403 travelling in the offside lane of the said road in the direction of Merton.

'Questioned at the scene you said, "I do not understand what has happened."'

I read the summons through again. Then I read it methodically sentence by sentence. After a time I went away and made myself another cup of coffee. Whatever famous people said, my own mind was obviously not at its nimblest at this time of day. Back in the sitting room I had found two matchboxes and was pushing them backwards and forwards on the carpet, laboriously trying to reconstruct the accident, when I was startled by a voice from the doorway saying something about fires. I looked up to see Mo, a statuesque vision with hair in giant rollers, face shiny with cream, wearing a little pink babydoll nightie and a saggy green cardigan as long as a coat. Swatches of cottonwool protruded from both her ears. She looked blearily down at me.

'Oh hello, it's you, Charlotte, is it? I was just saying, has there been a fire or something?'

'Not that I've noticed,' I said

'What d'you say? Oh, good. But if there hasn't been a fire,' she continued after a moment's thought, 'what the devil are you doing up in the middle of the night playing trains?'

'I'm not playing trains,' I said. 'I'm just working out a traffic accident.'

'Doing what?'

'Working,' I said more loudly.

'I can see for myself that you're lurking, but why? What d'you say? Cars? Well, cars then . . .'

'Do get that wool out of your ears, Mo. You're as deaf as a post.'

'What d'you say?'

I performed a brief pantomime, pulling enough imaginary wadding out of my own ears to have stuffed my entire head.

'Ah,' said Mo with ready comprehension, removing the cottonwool from one ear. 'That's better. I was having a bit of trouble hearing you before, to tell the truth.'

'What are you doing up yourself?' I asked. Mo was not by nature an early riser; each night's sleep closely resembled hibernation.

'Well, there was this terrible noise. I could hear fire engines or a burglar alarm or something, as clearly as if it was inside the flat. I don't suppose I'd have heard anything in the normal way but I couldn't find my earplugs last night and this cottonwool's nowhere near as good. I think I might have lost them down the back of the settee and I'd like to have them in case the fire engines come back. I'm not a heavy sleeper, you know, and it was quite terrifying to think of all those poor souls in the blaze. I couldn't take it twice.'

'I'm afraid it must have been my alarm clock you heard.'

'Your alarm clock? Good lord.' She stared at me, aghast. 'You know, the thing to do with a clock that makes a noise like that is to turn it off – not just . . . lie there and listen to it.'

'Well, you see, I always hide it,' I explained. 'Otherwise I tend to turn it off without waking up.'

'Next time I hear that thing,' Mo said bitterly, 'it will be a great pleasure to come in and chuck a bucket of cold water over you, just to make sure you're up and about. I'll make a point of it. And now, if you'll excuse me,' she added with dignity, 'I'll retire and leave you to your game of cars. You know, I don't envy you your job.'

She withdrew and I went back to my game of cars. Translated from police English into action, the facts of the case seemed fairly straightforward. My client had approached a dual carriageway along a minor side road, waited at the junction, and then chosen his moment to drive very slowly indeed into the fast lane, straight into the path of an oncoming sports car, which had been unable to avoid a collision. Miraculously nobody had been seriously hurt but my client had been charged with careless driving and I was bound to say that on these facts I could see no defence. Nor could I see any explanation for a plea of not guilty – unless Mr Pennyweather had a completely different version of the facts. Perhaps he would say that the sports-car driver had suddenly lost control and swerved into him, for example. Where was Mr Pennyweather's statement? I looked for it. There was none. I went back to my instructions:

> 'Whilst broadly accepting the facts alleged by the prosecution, the client has caused a plea of not guilty to be entered on his behalf and counsel is instructed strenuously to defend the charge. Those instructing understand that a point of principle is involved . . .'

A point of principle? What point of principle? I turned over the page but Mr Kenworth had run out of ideas at this point and signed off with a flourish. To me, the announcement of the presence of a point of law in a case has never been good for morale. But a point of law is like a snake: if you can find it, you can deal with it logically. A point of principle on the other hand defies logic, like the sea; the only thing to be done is to dive in and hope for the best. Perhaps Mr Pennyweather would come to court, like one of my previous careless driving clients, armed with dozens of measurements from which he hoped to establish that one of the streetlamps was five inches too far from its neighbour, or like another, who had twenty blurred snapshots showing how from just such an angle an oncoming lorry could be mistaken for a bollard. Points of principle always had to be argued 'strenuously', and although I had put up as fierce an argument as I could in both these past cases, the waste of time involved had led the bench to 'take a robust view of the circumstances' – or, in plain words, add ten pounds to the fine.

Having taken my own view of the circumstances, it seemed that the most helpful thing I could do for Mr Pennyweather would be to draft out the best possible plea in mitigation, but try as I might I could think of very little to say on his behalf. I would have to wait until I saw him at court. Perhaps he might have a clean driving licence or a wooden leg. Feeling that for now I had done all I could, I took the bacon and eggs to the kitchen and fried them. Heavy with breakfast, I presently set off for Waterloo station, caught the 8.37 and slept uneasily, waking myself at every station all the way to Epsom.

It was a raw grey morning, dank, with fog which eddied like cold smoke among the leafless treetops and drizzled over the greasy paving stones of the high street. Even after the short walk from the station I was glad to enter the stale half-warmth of the court antehall, where the usual morning shambles was in progress. In the press of jostling, steaming bodies everyone seemed to be hunting for someone or competing to be heard above the hubbub. Clients like lost baby birds rushed about searching for their lawyers; barristers and solicitors pushed through the crowd calling out the names of their clients and witnesses: and court officers shouted defendants' names from clipboard lists like a gaggle of town criers. I had heard from Freddy of a place in the Royal Courts of Justice called the Bear Garden where the pandemonium was worse than this — so dreadful, in fact, that solicitors' clerks had more than once had to be led away weeping. If it was really worse there than the average magistrates' court at half past nine, I could easily believe the story.

As I muscled into the fray, I scanned every corner for Mr Kenworth. I soon spotted him squeezed up against a radiator, hugging his briefcase defensively to his broad black bosom. I could see no signs of a client but it did seem that Mr Kenworth was talking to someone; by the look of things, it was not a conversation he was enjoying much, for he had a fugitive air as though he would have liked to filter his seventeen-stone bulk into a crack in the stonework. I pushed towards him through the tide of humanity. It was upstream all the way but I reached the radiator at last. Then I realized that Mr Pennyweather was indeed there but was so short that he had previously been completely hidden.

My client was oval in shape, tapering away at the bottom to a pair of high-sided patent pumps and at the top to a bald crown which shone with equal lustre. His Tweedledee appearance was made more striking by a bright green bowtie, a watch chain fastened about his broadest point and a red and silver spotted waistcoat. Against the drab decor he stood out like a newly minted Easter egg but the festive look stopped short of his face, which wore the petulant expression of a cross baby.

'Mr Pennyweather,' piped Mr Kenworth sadly, 'Miss Hunter.'

My client's face smoothed into cordial greeting. 'Ah, good day to you, dear lady, good day.' He extended a plump hand. 'Most pleased to meet you, most pleased, yes indeed.' He had a rather breathless way of speaking and a trick of repeating himself which made the most trivial utterance sound urgent and confidential. 'We have just been discussing my case, Mr Woolworth here and I, and I have had to point out to him how dissatisfied, how very dissatisfied, I am with the way in which it has been dealt with by the court, his firm in general and himself in particular.'

'I'm very sorry to hear that,' I said cautiously, hoping to find out as much as I could without appearing to take sides against Mr Kenworth. 'What's been the trouble exactly?'

I looked at Mr Kenworth, hoping for some quick and cogent explanation, but he seemed to have gone into temporary retirement, merely waving a dispirited hand in the direction of Mr Pennyweather, who took up the tale again.

'I think I can put the matter in a nutshell when I ask you to guess when I was notified of today's hearing. You'll be unable to credit it, I feel quite sure. Yes – only five days ago,' he went on, without pausing for an answer. 'Last Friday, to be exact. What do you think of that?'

Suddenly called on for an opinion, I found myself beset by indecision. Was five days' notice enough? I had no idea. If not, whose fault was it? If Mr Kenworth could be held to blame, I reasoned, I had better give a woolly answer. On the other hand, if I could think of some harmless scapegoat . . .

'Deplorable,' I said heatedly. 'I don't know what the court administrator can be coming to.'

Mr Pennyweather seemed pleased with this. 'Quite so, dear lady, exactly so. Just what I said myself.' He nodded the upper part of his oval form with approval before adding dishearteningly, 'And that piece of malpractice is the mere tip of the icebox, as the saying goes.'

'Oh dear,' I said, as warmly as I could.

'Yes, indeed. I am very sad to say,' went on my client, appearing anything but sad, 'that there are others at whom I must point my finger.'

He bent a dark glance upon Mr Kenworth, who recoiled at the threat.

Diplomatically I jumped to the defence. 'Er, I'm sure your solicitors did everything they could.'

'I daresay you feel bound to say so.' Mr Pennyweather batted this loose conversational ball to the boundary with a sound like a snort. 'I might have believed so previously but I have seen the light now, you may be sure; for what did I do on that Friday but throw down my shaving brush – I was shaving at the time – and rush out to the car with the lather still on my face. And where did I go?'

'I'm afraid I'm not sure.'

'You may well ask. Of course I drove at top speed to the offices of Woolworthy here, only to be told that he was out; on another case, if you please.'

Here he stared with disgust at poor Mr Kenworth, who tried with some success to camouflage himself against the background of government-green wall paint.

'I need hardly tell you, dear lady, how little reassurance it brings to be told that, instead of being at his proper post ready to take up the cudgels on one's behalf, one's legal representative has disappeared on some . . . frolic.'

The mental spectacle of Mr Kenworth in his black bowler frolicking round St Pancras Coroner's Court was almost more than I could bear.

'Well, you know, Mr Pennyweather, as Chief Managing and Administrative Litigation Clerk of the Motoring, Licensing and Family Law Departments, Mr Kenworth is a very busy man.' I hoped that this might at least be good for another brief from Wiseley's.

'I have never believed,' said Mr Pennyweather, 'that any good came of over-ambition. 'You mark my words, young man,' he added to Mr Kenworth, 'you'll never get anywhere if you persist in spreading yourself so thin that you're always disappearing and putting your clients to the inconvenience of searching for you. There are some of us, you know, who have better things to do than tear in and out of your offices with lather still on our faces.'

'Might I ask whether this has any direct bearing on your case?' I interposed. I was becoming worried that we might be called on at any moment and that at present my grip on this case was not strong.

Unfortunately the question seemed to vex Mr Pennyweather. 'I can see you don't believe me,' he said huffily. 'Well, as it happens, I have a witness, yes indeed. My wife is out in the car at this very moment. She's an invalid and movement is extremely painful to her, but she won't begrudge the effort, I feel sure.'

'I assure you, Mr Pennyweather, it's not at all necessary . . .'

He swept my objection aside with a wave of the hand. 'Nonsense, nonsense. It's a point of principle. I haven't come all this way to be called a liar.'

With this parting shot directed over his shoulder at Mr Kenworth, who so far had said nothing at all, the extraordinary little man sped out into the freezing fog and was lost to sight.

He returned very soon, supporting a fragile elderly lady, whom he set down tenderly on a bench. She folded her hands and sat looking at us with an air of mild expectation.

'My wife,' he said in an aside to us. Then, turning to the old lady, said loudly: 'Now, Mother, I've just been telling this lady and, er, person about what happened last Friday.'

'Last Friday?'

'Yes, that's right, last Friday morning. Now just you speak up and tell them what happened when I got that summons through the post.'

He stood back slightly in the manner of an advocate producing a star witness. A silence fell.

'Well, come along, my dear,' he prompted. 'Tell them what I did.'

'I don't think you did anything, Alfred,' she said after a few moments' consideration. 'Nothing particular, that is. We had kipper for breakfast, I remember . . .'

'Yes now, think carefully, my dear; cast your mind back. You must recall me shaving.'

'I expect you were, dear, if you say so.'

'And you brought up that brown envelope. I daresay you remember that?'

'What a keen memory you have, Alfred.'

'And did I, my dear, or did I not throw down the brush and run out to the car with my face all over lather?'

The old lady looked faintly scandalized. 'Of course not, Alfred. Why ever would you want to do such a thing? Dear me no. You came down as usual and ate your breakfast. As a matter of fact, now I think I recall you saying the kipper was rather greasy, and I said . . .'

'That will do very well, Mother,' interposed her husband.

She gave him a gentle smile. 'It was fortunate I came, wasn't it, dear?' she said.

As the point of principle subsided under this death blow, I seized the moment to ask Mr Pennyweather some questions about the accident. The facts were as I had surmised. My client agreed that he had crossed the double-dotted lines at the junction, driven into the fast lane and been in collision with the sports car which he had clearly failed to notice.

'And they've charged me with careless driving!' he said in outrage. 'Whatever do you think of that?'

I thought he was very lucky not to have been killed but it seemed hardly tactful to say so.

'However, that to my mind is by no means the worst aspect, dear lady, although you may find it hard to credit . . .' He was right. I did indeed find it hard to believe that there could be anything worse.

'For now that I at last meet Mr Woolworth,' said my client 'what does he do? You may well wonder. Does he stand behind me, bear me up and range himself shoulder to shoulder with me as he should? Not at all. It may surprise you to hear, dear lady, that Woolworth has given it as his opinion this morning that I should lie prone before the bench and bare my breast to judgement.'

To hear that Mr Kenworth had advised in such epic terms was certainly a surprise. 'Did he really say that?'

'"Put your hands up to the charge, Mr Pennyweather." Those were his very words. They dashed the breath from my body, dear lady, the very breath.'

At this moment I confess to wishing that that had been true.

'Before I give you my own advice, just let me get things straight,' I said. 'This bit of road, do you know it well?'

'Backwards. I travel the same way every day.'

'And do you often do that – go straight into the fast lane as you did on this occasion?'

'Invariably.'

'Oh yes, I see. And why exactly do you always do that?'

'For purposes,' he said grandly, 'of road safety.'

'I wonder if you could perhaps expand on that a little?'

'Certainly. You see, I have to turn right about three quarters of a mile further on. How do I know that when I reach the turn there won't be some other vehicle coming up behind me in the fast lane? No. I take up my position in good time and travel along at a safe speed until I reach the turn. No purpose is served by taking risks.'

'By a safe speed you mean, what, about twenty-five miles an hour?'

'Certainly. I have never believed that any good came of darting about at excessive speed.'

'And since you started driving you've never had a single accident?'

'Never. I would venture to say that if more motorists drove as I do the road would be a very different place.'

I considered this as a point in mitigation and rejected it. 'But unfortunately on this occasion there was something coming in the fast lane?'

'That I don't admit.'

'I'm sorry?'

'Had it been coming, dear lady, rest assured that I would undoubtedly have seen it.'

'But it must have been. It ran into your car.'

'Well, perhaps it may have been coming,' he conceded at last, 'but, if it was, events have proved that it must have been travelling a good deal too fast. If it had been going at the same speed as I was, we would never have collided.'

Finding this unanswerable, I decided on another line of questioning. 'Have you any independent witnesses, other than Mrs Pennyweather, I mean, who might have seen the accident?'

'My dear madam,' he replied with dignity, 'the court will accept my sworn word without the least need for witnesses. I am certain that I have only to stand up and give my account of the matter and the bench will come to the proper decision.'

I was certain of it too, my only lingering doubt being about whether my client would be ordered to take a driving test or disqualified for life. At all costs he must be kept out of the witness-box, but in order to do that I had to persuade him to change his plea to guilty.

I set to work. In painstaking detail I explained the law of careless driving; point by point I demonstrated in what respects his driving had been careless, mentioning as an extra incentive that if the bench thought we had wasted time by contesting a hopeless case they might take a robust view of the circumstances. Mr Pennyweather heard me out in silence and I saw that my arguments were gradually having their effect. Well, they must, I reasoned. This man was no fool and anyone with an ounce of logic must be able to grasp that what I was saying was right. It was just a matter of time and patience. At last I felt that this unruly case was taking shape. Sure enough, when I came to the end my client nodded in unwilling agreement.

'A very cogent explanation, dear lady. I accept it without reservation. Yes indeed, without any reservation whatsoever.'

'Well, that's fine, Mr Pennyweather. I always feel it's important that my clients should understand not only what my advice is but why I am advising them to take a particular course,' I said with a touch of professional patronage. 'I'll just go and notify the court that you're pleading guilty and perhaps they'll take us in a bit earlier.'

'Plead guilty? Out of the question.'

The words came out in a stentorian squeak that stopped me in my tracks.

'I'm sorry, what was that?'

'Impossible, dear lady. Quite impossible.'

My trust in the power of logic had been over-optimistic.

'Let's look at the law again, Mr Pennyweather. You see, a driver's duty . . .'

'The question of driving is irrelevant.' My client swept motoring matters aside with a grand gesture. 'If you tell me that the law takes no account of extra foresight like mine, so be it. I don't pretend to understand it; but I accept. No, the point at issue is something quite different. You can call it another point of principle, if you like.'

Another point of principle? I could think of a number of things I might have liked to call it.

'Yes, indeed. What I am really concerned with is the blackguardly libel started up against me by the police.'

My heart sank to my black professional shoes. 'What libel is this, Mr Pennyweather?' I had no ambitions to set myself up as the Gerald Dodgwick of the police courts. 'What have the police been saying?'

'They say,' my client informed me in a voice quivering with indignation, 'that I left the car after the accident by climbing over my wife in the passenger seat. Think of it. Climbing over my wife. You have seen my wife; you have seen me. Do I look the sort of person who would scramble over a person, and an invalid at that? The very thought is outrageous. How could I possibly be expected to plead guilty to such a thing? I cannot and will not do it.'

He had taken up a pose which reminded me of a Roman hero being offered a dose of hemlock.

It was at about this stage that I realized that Mr Kenworth had disappeared. I hadn't noticed him go; he could move very silently on his big black feet. After everything he had been through this morning I could hardly blame him, but I felt deserted. As I tried to smooth down the irate Mr Pennywather I acknowledged to myself that, although my colleague had so far neither said nor done anything at all, I had found his silent presence a support.

I had given up all hope of a sensible resolution to the case and was explaining to Mr Pennyweather the procedure for taking the witness oath when, to my great relief, I caught sight of the airship figure of Mr Kenworth drifting back across the hallway towards us. He was accompanied by a stout uniformed police officer.

'Miss Hunter, PC James, prosecuting officer in the case. May be some assistance,' whispered Mr Kenworth in telegrammatic style and quietly reattached himself to the wall.

'Well, madam, old George there, that's to say your instructing solicitor, and I have been having some discussion about this case, from which I understand that a plea of guilty may be forthcoming.'

'I'm afraid I couldn't go so far . . .'

'In which eventuality I believe I would be entitled to assume the authority of the Metropolitan Police Commissioner to withdraw any allegation which might have been made as to the defendant's manner of leaving the vehicle and also, with regard to such allegation, to offer this gentleman and his wife an unconditional apology.'

Mr Pennyweather's plea of guilty went surprisingly well. I was able to point to his unimpeachable driving record of thirty years, which was evidence more of miraculous good fortune than of good driving, had the bench but known it. He came away with a ten-pound fine and seemed delighted with the result. 'Thank you, thank you, dear lady,' he said, wringing me enthusiastically by the hand. 'A tour de force, a real tour de force. Yes, indeed. "English law is the nest of justice", as the saying goes, and this morning has made me her true devotee.'

I felt like a cuckoo in that nest, accepting praise which rightfully belonged to Mr Kenworth, whose shrewd diplomacy had saved the day for our client. Logic and the law, I was coming to realize, did not always pull in double harness, especially where principles were involved.

Having shaken my hand a final time, the devotee of justice turned and let his eye travel up the towering silent bulk of the true author of the tour de force, the Chief Managing Litigation Clerk of Wisely & Wiseley's Motoring Department.

'Whippersnapper,' said Mr Pennyweather.

With a look of withering scorn he put his hand behind his back. 'I don't shake hands with your kind,' he added, '. . . as a matter of principle.'

14

'. . . Fatima Jessop's famous charm made the blemishes fly from the back of my neck so I can now face it in the mirror . . .

'. . . Quite remarkable. Thanks to Fatima Jessop I can at last Vouch for my Feet . . .'

'Vulgar nonsense. What are you trying to do, Percival, sully my hard-built reputation in a single morning? "Vouch for my feet", indeed. Words fail me, Percival, they really do.'

It was rare to see my pupilmaster ruffled. With an expression of wounded surprise the walrus put down the bottle he was carrying in such a position that the label showed, spread both flippers on the tooled leather surface of the great desk and thrust his whiskered face forward almost into Freddy's, shaking his jowls in a solicitous manner.

'Hff. All grist to the mill, sir,' he remarked in his hollow voice.

'But to whose mill? There's something fishy about this.' Freddy looked severely at the walrus. 'And you needn't try to draw my fire by bringing bottles in here . . . Well, no harm in trying, I suppose. Is that the Napoleon? No, no, leave it here. I may feel strong enough to manage a mouthful after dinner. Meanwhile, Percival, what do you mean by foisting on me a piece of such unspeakable . . . silliness?' He tapped the papers in front of him.

'It's marked at seventy-five guineas, sir,' said the walrus, 'which is on the plus side, you'll agree. Furthermore . . .'

'On the minus side, Percival,' cut in Freddy, 'it is in the Devizes County Court, a full two and a half hour hegira away; it is a possession action – how long it may have been since I last did a possession I cannot say. Worse, it is a defended matter turning upon the live issue of whether a lady who charms warts . . . warts, Percival – by post can be said to be carrying on a business within the meaning of the Landlord and Tenant Act. Can you wonder I am speechless?'

'Did you say charms warts?' I asked.

'I did, heaven help me; and also, according to the testimonials, carbuncles and assorted blemishes of one kind and another. I would appreciate it, young Charlotte, if you would desist from sniggering in that uncivil way.'

'I'm so sorry, but you've no idea what a comfort it is to see someone else get an odd case once in a while,' I said. 'I never seem to get a case that's quite normal.'

'I'm not convinced there is such a thing,' said Freddy, momentarily deflected. 'Any more than there is such a thing as a strictly normal person, I suppose. It's no bad thing, anyway, for a person newly called such as yourself, dear girl, to be the butt of a certain amount of ridicule; it's good for the soul, an innoculation against conceit. At a later stage, however, reputation is a fragile bloom.'

He took a sudden lyrical turn. 'I am, Percival, as you know, a modest man against whose grain it goes to lay emphasis on such trifling matters as professional standing, but I shouldn't object to hearing what's behind this nonsense, if you please.'

'Who, sir,' said the walrus informatively.

'What do you mean who? It's no good asking me. You know I don't know anything about it; I'm asking you.'

'No, sir, in other words, it's not what's behind it but who's behind it,' explained the walrus.

'Well, who is behind it then? I am not a bad-tempered man, Percival, but once aroused I am terrible. I'm warning you now.'

'In a word, Mr Lamb, sir,' said the walrus.

'What, of Lamb Griffin? Ah well, I owe you an apology, Percival,' said Freddy. 'I was beginning to suspect that that disreputable friend of Norman's neighbour was embroiled in another legal problem requiring free advice and help.'

'He's gone away, sir, I understand.'

'What, Brixton? Parkhurst? I won't ask where or deny that the news gladdens my heart. To return to our muttons . . .'

'Plaintiff's a close personal friend of Mr Lamb apparently. I understand Mr Lamb was very pleased with your handling of that foreign client, I forget his name. This is a sign of appreciation, if you like.'

'Great heaven,' said my pupilmaster faintly. 'If this is a token of esteem, I hope to stay out of old Lamb's black books.'

'Perhaps it'll settle, sir,' the Walrus suggested. 'Then you'll have the rest of the day to knock off that urgent set for Wiseley's. No good just giving your papers a change of air, sir, as I often tell you.'

'I can't see it settling unless the defendant caves in. She hasn't a leg to stand on as at present advised.'

'Well, you'll just have to roll your sleeves up in the evening, won't you, sir? Speedy and deedy . . . Well now, I must say goodbye,' said the walrus, noticing Freddy's fingers curling round a paperknife. He unhitched his fins from the desk and stood up.

'Oh, Miss Hunter, I rather think there may be something on for you too tomorrow.' With an agility surprising in one of his huge size, he departed, to be seen some time later making his way up the steps outside my window, where already the lamplighter with his long pole was beginning to touch the gas streetlights into life. Bound for El Vino's I expected, to continue his long day's work.

'What have you got there, young Hunter?' my pupilmaster inquired as I came back with the next day's brief. 'Trying to get possession of a flat? Is the tenant defending? No. Well, that's always helpful. What can I tell you? Not a great deal. If the Rent Acts apply, you'll have to show that the premises are furnished, right? And you show that by . . . doing what? By finding out the value of the furniture, or something of the kind; there's a formula but it seems to have slipped my mind. You'll soon find it in *Hill & Redman*, I daresay. There's a case, what was it: *Clopman* or *Coutts* perhaps? Great heaven, listen to this: "It is thanks to Fatima Jessop that I have been able to return to my work as a strip-club hostess."'

'These revelations, my dear Freddy, while undeniably fascinating, may not perhaps be in the best of taste.' David Jermaine strolled across to Freddy's desk and twitched the sheet of paper from his hand.

'Thanks to Fatima Jessop I can at last . . .' Do what? "Vouch for my Feet"? Doesn't sound your usual line of country at all, Fred. Your practice must be on the decline, dear fellow.'

'Have you come for some honest purpose other than to weep crocodile tears over the state of my practice?' Freddy inquired.

'Yes, indeed. Away with these frivolities. I'm after a quantum, if you can spare a moment.'

A quantum is the barrister's phrase for an educated guess as to the amount of damages likely to be awarded in a case.

'Here you are, two medical reports. Very much obliged. I shall now do my best to assist by sinking into an intense silence. Poor devil fell into an industrial fishpaste mixer,' he added in a loud aside to me. 'Nasty injuries to an arm and an ankle, and the prognosis isn't too good either. Still, could have been worse – doesn't bear thinking of . . . all those little jars. Well, young Charlotte, what have you got on tomorrow? Going to watch your pupilmaster dispossess the lady?'

'I'd have liked to. I've never seen a wart charmer before.'

'I saw one once in a bazaar somewhere,' David said reminiscently. 'One of those ascetic-looking types in a diaper blowing a penny whistle at the warts or whatever they were, or could it have been snakes? Ah well, warts, snakes, how memory fails one . . . Finished yet, Tobin? Can't dawdle about here all day you know. I'm in a tearing hurry.' He disposed his long limbs more comfortably over the arm of the wing chair and picked up a copy of *The Times* from the table.

'This lady defendant of Freddy's cures warts by post,' I said. 'All you do is send your name, address and some nail parings . . .'

'My dear girl,' said David Jermaine, raising a languid hand. 'I refuse to hear any more of your maunderings on such topics. I may not look it, but a more refined and sensitive soul never lived. What's that you've got there? A possession? Your own? Good show. Now how does it go . . . You've got to establish that it's furnished, as I remember. Isn't there some useful formula or other which never fails? Afraid it has slipped my mind. Too much water under the old bridge . . .'

'Or burgundy?'

'Speak for yourself, Frederick,' said David without rancour. 'Ah, finished at last? Good show. Jot it down on here.' He handed a slip of paper across the desk and dug a number of similar slips from his pocket. 'Now let's see, what have we got? Obviously this is general damages only. Mike said five thousand; Owen thought between eight and ten – he's very good on quantum; Bill, eleven five – a bit high that one, I'd have said; and your was?'

'Six to seven was the best I could say; that's on full liability.'

'Well, that's er . . .'

'Hardly helpful,' Freddy said.

'Well no, I don't think it is. It's more what I'd call a broad spectrum of opinion. No bloody good at all, in fact.'

'In other words you're thrown back on *Current Law* or your own guesswork?'

'Good lord no,' said Jermaine. 'Before going to either such extreme, I think I'll take the views of Jim and Graham. Now I think of it, they're more likely to be up with present lines of thinking that the old guard.'

'What do you mean old guard?' asked Freddy in disgust. 'It makes us sound like a lot of Boer War veterans; old, crabbed, reactionary . . .'

'If the cap fits, old boy . . .'

'I warn you,' said my much-tried pupilmaster. 'I'm not a bad-tempered man but once aroused I am terrible . . .'

'I think I'll say goodbye,' said David Jermaine. 'Off to broaden my spectrum. Oh, while I think of it, Norman was wanting a word with you just now. Told me to tell you Wiseley's were on, rather heated about some urgent set of papers.'

'I'm going home,' said Freddy Tobin . . .

'What have you got there, Charlotte?' asked Graham. 'A Rent Act case? Don't you have to prove the flat's furnished? There's some formula or other; you'll probably find it in *Megarry*. Whatever you do, don't forget to deal with the furniture.

'Thanks, I won't,' I said. 'By the way, did you give David a quantum just now?'

'Yes. I said fifteen thousand, as far as I remember. I was out on a limb apparently and not much help.'

'Is that what David said?'

'Yes, he said the old guard knew best, whoever they may be.'

One irritating event is only too likely to open the floodgates on a whole host of other unwelcome happenings. If the overflow pipe overflows, fanbelts also burst, heavy objects fall on bare feet, bank managers put pen to paper. The next morning ripened quickly into one of those days when I knew I was to be the innocent victim of fate. Why today of all days, for example, had the electric kettle fused? For the same sinister reason that the tube trains refused to come and skulked in their tunnels, splitting their scaly sides with glee, no doubt. Again, as part of this vendetta, the ticket collector at Paddington had refused to let me on the train without a ticket, so that I missed the fast train and had to travel instead on something unheated, which stopped like a dog at every lamp-post and set the seal on an undistinguished performance by succumbing to engine failure outside Reading. It was in no very good temper, therefore, that I at last arrived at Burnham Halt, chilled through and well on the way to being late.

The relief train snaked away, leaving me alone on the long platform. I picked up my blue bag and briefcase and started walking. It was a good three-minute trudge to the ticket barrier. This was deserted, but next to it was a shedlike building in which sat an old man in uniform reading a paper. I asked if there was a taxi to be had.

'What d'you say?'

I repeated the request. The old man rasped his chin with a horny thumb and forefinger. No, there was nothing like that to be found hereabouts. I might as well have been asking the time of the next carpet to Turkestan.

'Can you tell me how to get to the town?' I asked.

'Eh?'

'The town?'

'Which town?'

'Is there more than one?'

'Not that I know of.' The old man rose and came to the door, pointing a hand out across the ploughed fields low-hung with mist which stretched away on every side. 'Over the stile, three fields and past the coppice'll bring ye to a track. Right and then left tord the church steeple until ye reach the stepping stoans and after next stile ye'll see the fingerpost. Can't miss it.'

'How long would it take to walk?'

The old man considered this. 'Dunno,' he said. 'That's the short cut.'

I am not a keen walker and the idea of trekking through the winter fields in my high-heeled shoes and laden with baggage struck me as not only unappealing but foolhardy. There just be some alternative. Perhaps I could find a telephone and call a mini-cab?

'Excuse me, where's the nearest telephone?'

'Eh?'

I bellowed out a repetition. This time the old man pointed in the opposite direction across the tracks to where, beyond the earthen shoulder of a small hill, the top of a telephone box could just be seen as a red pimple upon the grey-brown landscape.

'Excuse me, is there a bridge over the tracks?'

'Eh?'

I would have felt conspicuous stumbling across the tracks with all my baggage had there been anyone there to see, but the old man had gone in again to his stove and in all the winter morning there was only myself and the rooks.

Five minutes of cloggy walking brought me to my objective. Shards of broken glass littered the concrete floor and through the gaping holes in the panes I could see the receiver hanging limp and dislocated from the remains of a machine which had suffered death by violence. It twirled gently in the cold air, stirred by my passing. Unspeakably depressed, I made my way back to the station. Railroad Bill was still sitting potbellied by the stove reading a magazine.

'Eh?'

'Vandalized,' I shouted. 'Broken up.'

'Ay, yes I know,' remarked the old man. 'Wicked in't it?'

'But, if you knew, why didn't you say?' I said in exasperation.

'Eh? No business o'mine. Ye asked for the nearest box and I tell't ye. Are ye off this time? Over the stile then, three fields and past the coppice . . .'

Half an hour, three stiles, a stream and a forestation of bramble bushes later I reached the fingerpost. It was lying flat on its back in the ditch. I could remember learning as a small child at school that the thing to do in such circumstances was to set it up again so that the arm bearing the name of the place one had been pointed in the direction one had come from. This piece of information, which I had apparently hoarded up for years in some dark corner of my mind, would have been more useful if I had known either where I had been or whether King's Clippings, Queen's Clippings or Abbott's Clippings was nearest to the town. I looked at my watch. Ten past ten. Twenty minutes to go and no sign of civilization anywhere; nothing but the flat winter landscape, a sweep of ploughed furrows, grey hedgerows humped against the mist, grasses laden with cold pearls of dew shivering on the banks of the rumbling road . . . The rumbling road? With a sudden upsurge of hope I craned my neck to see over the top of a high grassy ridge. Something was coming. A bus? It was: a green country bus coming my way. Could it be going to the town? Did it matter where it was bound so long as it was going somewhere else? Hastily I stepped into the middle of the road and stood spreadeagled, holding my wig-bag in one hand and my briefcase in the other. Had my luck changed at last?

'Please, do you go to the Burnham County Court?'

'You mean the magistrates' court,' the conductor said.

'No. The county court, please.'

'What's that? You mean the town hall.'

'No. The county court.'

'Two and ninepence,' said the conductor, making it clear that the offer was final. 'Two and threepence change.'

'Could you tell me when we get there please?'

'Where? The town hall or the police court?'

'Whichever's closer,' I said.

The bus rumbled on between high banks edged with trees whose bare branches slapped and squeaked against the windows. After a time the lane broadened out and we were slipping between garden hedges of clipped evergreen. I leaned my head against the cold window glass, relieved and glad to rest. We must be nearly there. I would be just on time.

When I awoke the bus was in open country once more. A thin bright shaft had straggled through the clouds giving an impression of mid-morning. I looked at my watch. Five past eleven. Horrified, I shot to my feet and began blundering up the aisle with my bags. I must get off; at all costs I must somehow get back to the town again. Beastly visions crowded into my mind: of a judge purple-faced with indignation; of clients and solicitors running desperately about; frantic telephone calls to chambers, to the flat; of the apologies I should have to make; the mortification, the disgrace . . .

'Oh, it's you,' said the conductor. 'That reminds me. Shame. Still, there's a bus the other way. Goes once an hour.'

'When's the next?' I panted.

'Shame. We just passed it.'

I started walking again. A little thin wind had sprung up, numbing my fingers and the tip of my long nose. Tears of self-pity pricked my eyes, welled up and rolled down my cheeks. Ashamed of myself, I stopped and pulled out a paper handkerchief. On a low wall on the other side of the lane someone had painted in rough white capitals:

REFUSE TO BE PLACED IN PLASTIC SACK
AND LEFT HERE FOR COLLECTION.

In a strange way this firmed my resolve. Yes, I would refuse. Cold, tired and late though I was, I had not yet come to that. I plodded on again. The court couldn't be far now – or, at any rate, something couldn't.

Some way down the road I made out through the thinning mist the sound of a car approaching from behind. What if I stopped it and asked for a lift? I had never hitch-hiked in my life, feeling one could never be too careful, but this was an emergency. Surely no motorist would try to take advantage of a woman lawyer complete with wig-bag and briefcase and, above all, wearing my Bulgarian suit? I stepped into the road waving. The car, a red Mini, came to a halt and a female face looked out from among a jumble of small children and dogs. I stated my business. The woman looked me over from pale blue eyes.

'The court? Oh, not far, no more than a mile. I wish I could offer you a lift but, I'm sure you understand, I make it a rule never to pick up hitchhikers. One can't be too careful.'

Too nonplussed to speak, I stood in the road and watched her drive away. What kind of desperado had that rude woman taken me for? A modern highwayman's moll? My black breast heaved with indignation. A kidnapper, perhaps? Wearily I had set off again when it occurred to me that in a way she had paid me a compliment: if I still looked energetic enough to do the woman, the children and all those dogs a mischief, I must be a good deal fitter than I had ever imagined.

Then round a corner I saw it: the county court. Suspiciously I stared at it from across the road. Was it the town hall in disguise? A mirage, perhaps? No, it was the real thing: an architectural feature even, large as life and twice as solid. . . . And standing next door to the town's main railway station.

Silently I shouted with mirth. Whoever said 'you got to laugh or you'd cry' was absolutely right.

By this time it was nearly half past eleven. The antehall, a draughty place done up in anaglypta wallpaper varnished to resemble wood, was surprisingly crowded in view of the time and I found this comforting, for I had expected everybody to have gone home. I stood by the noticeboard with my brief in my hand feeling a little lost and wondering if I should shout out the name of my client. If so, how was the name Czyzewski pronounced? I had just about decided to try 'Sizifsky' when a squat young man with shaggy brown hair approached and introduced himself as Mr Boland of Holt & Goodbody. He must have been about twenty and was dashingly dressed in a long green anorak, nylon trousers with a red and brown tweed design, and a shiny grey tie of which the knot hung at breastbone level in the manner favoured by Paul, the junior clerk.

I embarked on a trailing explanation of my lateness but had not got very far when the young man silenced me with a raised hand and a friendly if mysterious wink, and said out of the corner of his mouth, 'No hassle. Never mind about that. We've got real problems.'

'Oh dear, have we?' I said worriedly. 'What problems?'

'Old Zoosky the plaintiff can't speak a word. Might as well expect the gatepost to give evidence.'

'Oh dear, is he handicapped?'

'No, at least not physically. He's foreign.'

'I see, and he doesn't speak English?'

'Keine un mot. It's a bit of a cods-up. There should be an interpreter.'

'What language does he speak?' I asked.

'Serbish, did he say? Something like that. Thing is, he's dead against putting the case off. I suggested we adjourn in order to get hold of an interpreter but he wants the tenant ordered out, and of course he's be entitled to a twenty-eight-day order for possession. Tenant's committed every breach of covenant short of keeping pigs on the premises and isn't even defending. It's open and shut.'

'Well, quite.'

'Client says the family are having hysterics over the whole thing. Mind you, I shouldn't think that's anything unusual. They're a pretty weird lot.'

'How did he tell you all this if he doesn't speak English?'

'He's brought his daughter, Mrs Czernuszewicz,' he said, pronouncing it Zernoozywits. 'Her English isn't so bad.'

'That puts a different complexion on it,' I suggested.

'Trouble with her, she's dotty,' contributed Mr Boland. 'We're next on, by the way.' He pointed to the list. 'This one, *Ravitch* v. *Kirklefsky*, has just been called.'

I noticed that he had extremely long nails, and wondered what he did in his spare time. They were obviously occupational; it would be impossible to grow nails like that unintentionally. Perhaps he played the harp?

'The only way we'll be able to do anything today is if Mrs Zernoozywits acts as interpreter,' I said.

'Oh, I don't know if the judge'd wear that.' From his tone he might have been speaking of an item of ladies underwear. 'Come along anyway, I'll introduce you. They're all over here . . .' ('And the best of British luck,' I thought I heard him add under his breath as we moved towards a crowd of people milling about in one corner of the hallway and all furiously talking at once.) 'Miss Hunter, Mr Zoosky, Mrs Zernoozywits. The others all seem to be relatives,' he explained, indicating the crowd with a flash of his lustrous claws.

My client was sitting in the middle of the scrum on top of a table: a heavy sad-faced man with an ancestral beard in black and grey stripes and by contrast a head as innocent of hair as the dome of St Paul's. His daughter was a small black-haired woman in a flowered print dress with snapping eyes and pointed teeth. She gave an impression of great energy, bobbing about the crowd as though she could hardly keep still and talking excitedly in a hoarse and complicated tongue.

I soon found that communicating with my client was an almost impossible problem. This was partly because of the loud noise the crowd was making and partly because of some quality of Mrs Czernuszewicz's translations which produced unpredictable results. When I apologized for my late arrival, for example, my client looked annoyed and put a number of obviously searching questions to his daughter; on the other hand, to my comment that he must prepare himself for the disappointment of an adjournment, his response was to smile, wink broadly and slap his knee. More than once the interpreter enlisted the support of the crowd, who joined in with a great gust of discussion and dispute.

Thinking to have a last glance in peace at my notes on procedure I took refuge in the barristers' robing room but the whole lot of them stuffed in behind me and stood watching me struggling with the wing collar – laying bets on the winner, by the sound of it, and arguing angrily about the proper way to stick in the studs. In the end I suggested that Mr Boland show them all into court.

When I followed a few minutes later the case of *Ravitch* v. *Kirklefsky* was still going on. The two bearded contestants sitting in boxes on either side of the bench provided an almost biblical contrast: the landlord smooth and fat in a coat with a fur collar; his tenant in a miserable patched mac and holey cardigan. The judge, who sat between them making notes, appeared to be re-fereeing the fighting-out of an old contest.

'You want to hear why I don't pay your rent, Ravitch? You want I should tell you, eh?'

'I don't want you should tell me nothing, Kirklevsky. I want tragedies, I go to the film; I want rent, I go to the court. Pay up, Kirklevsky, and we go home for lunch.'

'I suppose you want I should pay extra for the mouses?'

'Ha. A joke,' said Mr Ravitch with ready perception. 'That I should be so lucky to fiddle away my time making jokes.' He threw both gloved hands into the air in a parody of joie de vivre. 'That I should be so blessed to laugh all the day like you!'

'If you had in your flat the crowd of mouses I have in my room then you would laugh on the other side of your head, Ravitch,' prophesied the tenant darkly. 'Old twister. Honest, my lordship, what I have to suffer. I go in my bed; I hear the mouses, nibble nibble in the wall bricks; nibble nibble in the roof; knock knock under the floor; scritch scratch everywhere, thumping to come in. Look, look, I brought my new sweater, bought only last week from Mocks & Spencer and left on my chair one night, one night . . . Look what your mouses done, Ravitch.'

He pulled from a plastic carrier bag something navy blue and woolly and with a sudden dramatic gesture whirled it into the air.

'Other side, Kirklevsky,' hissed his opponent. 'You always were a fool.'

'Ah, thanks.' The tenant turned the sweater round to reveal a large ragged hole.

'Yes, there, Ravitch. Teeth marks. Just look what your mouses done.'

'Pay up, Kirklevsky,' said the landlord, unimpressed. 'Pay up, we go home and I buy a micetrap.'

'Not enough, Ravitch.'

'Pay up and I buy half your sweater.'

'Two micetraps and all the sweater.'

'Kirklevsky, what you want to do to me? You think I am made with money? Whose mices are these, anyway? Not my mices, your mices. Who goes nibble nibble? Not the mices; you, Kirklevsky. Who is the one eating all the time cookies in bed, eh? Making what? . . . Crumps. Crumps in the bed, crumps in the carpet. I ask you, Kirklevsky, with crumps everywhere, is it my fault if you got what you say you got. How you say . . .' He brought it out with a flourish. '. . . Superfluous mice?'

After more negotiation there was a settlement based on two mousestraps and half the value of the sweater and the two combatants left the court apparently on the best of terms.

I felt the familiar tightening of my stomach as I checked the page in my notebook and spread out the particulars of claim. At first all went surprisingly well. To my relief, the defendant had not come to court, so that all I had to do to win was to go through the formalities. In addition the judge rather unexpectedly agreed to allow Mrs Czernuszewicz to act as unofficial interpreter.

'Very well, Miss Hunter, let's get on. Call your client.'

Mr Czyzewski moved heavily up the aisle with Mrs Czernuszewicz in attendance like a bridesmaid. While they were being sworn, I consulted my notebook to see what to do next. *Deal with furniture*. At first sight that was not very helpful. Rather doubtfully I looked at the three-page list of items ranging from 'Lounge: 1 arm. ch., approx. £15,' to 'Ktchn: 1 egg winder, approx. 2s 6d', wondering in what way I should set about making it part of the evidence. To this day I cannot say why it never occurred to me to have the whole list shown to the witness and say, 'Have you prepared and do you now produce this list of furniture in the premises?' or something of the sort. If I had only done that, all my troubles would have been avoided. Instead, I took a deep breath and shambled off down the road to disaster.

'Er, Mr Czyzewski, in the lounge, was there an armchair?'

'Oh yais,' said the interpreter. 'Was planty chairs. Planty.'

'Would you mind asking Mr Czyzewski?'

The interpreter shrugged as though surprised to have her word doubted, but turned and unloosed a hailstorm of words upon her father.

'Na,' said Mr Czyzewski.

Another barrage of words followed.

'Na,' said the witness, shaking his head ponderously from side to side. 'Na, na, nicht.'

'Ee say yais,' said the interpreter.

Rather surprisingly the judge let this pass.

I hurried on. 'Um, was there a table in the lounge?'

'Yais,' said the interpreter. 'Was planty.'

'Could you, er . . .' I pointed towards the witness.

Again the woman shrugged, turned to her father and put the question with explosive force. 'Na,' said the man, then something which sounded like 'nochtbocht'. The interpreter came in with another flood but the witness seemed to stand firm. 'Nochtbocht. Na, na, nichtbod.'

'Yaya, Papa . . .'

'Na.'

'Ee say yais,' said Mrs Czernuszewicz.

'Why does the witness keep shaking his head like that if he agrees with what you're putting to him?' asked the judge, entering the arena unexpectedly.

'Ee shek is aid for say yais,' offered the interpreter, but the judge did not seem entirely convinced.

'Was there a lamp?' I rushed back into the breach.

'Yais. Was planty lemps. Planty.'

'Na, nich nochbocht,' said the witness, not mincing matters. 'Na.'

'Ee say was planty lemps.'

'Miss Hunter,' said the judge. 'It appears to me that the interpreter is, er, prompting the witness. If there is any repetition of this behaviour, I shall have to, er, discipline the interpreter. It won't do, you know, madam, do you hear?'

'How much do you think the sofa was worth?' I soldiered on.

' . . . Yaya, Papa, feeftin pund, seextin pund . . .'

'Na, na, tree pund, tree pund.'

'Ee say was twanty pund,' reported Mrs Czernuszewicz.

'Madam,' said the judge, whose patience had by now worn thin, 'I have already had occasion to warn you about your, er, irregular behaviour; you have seen fit to ignore that warning. You will not be allowed to play ducks and drakes with this court. You will go to stand at the back of the courtroom and I hope it will teach you a lesson.'

It was doubtful how much of this the interpreter understood. Looking rather surprised, she allowed herself to be conducted by the usher to a position next to the exit doors at the far end of the court. Quite what the judge had intended to achieve by this draconian measure was not clear but the practical effects were awful.

'Er, was there a bookshelf in the lounge?' I asked the witness.

'Eh?' shouted the interpreter from afar.

'Was there a bookshelf?' I bellowed.

'Planty, planty cushions. Hola, Papa!'

'Eh?'

I realized with a sinking of the heart that we were still only in the lounge. There were four more rooms to go, not counting the broom cupboard.

'Was there a stool?' I yowled.

'Hola, Papa!'

'Miss Hunter, this is abominable. I must say that I have never before come across a case like this,' said the judge, blaming me – rather unfairly, I thought – for the unsatisfactory turn the proceedings had taken.

'Eh?' shouted the interpreter.

'I absolutely decline to hear any more of this,' said the judge with finality. I adjourn this matter for three weeks, costs in the cause, and may I add that I devoutly hope that during that time the parties may reach a settlement.'

Peeking out through a crack in the robing-room door I saw them all standing in a corner of the hallway arguing once more. It seemed to my fevered imagination that the crowd had grown larger and from the flurry of claws I glimpsed from its centre I knew that Mr Boland was somewhere in there trying to explain. Judging by the noise the crowd was making he did not seem to be getting on very well. They were waiting for me. Hidden behind the door I reviewed my situation. To make a bolt for it now would be a dreadful act of cowardice. Besides, I might never get another brief from Holt & Goodbody. Swiftly I weighed this possibility against the certainty of having to go out there and explain.

Na, nichbocht.

Resembling a war-tent in my greatcoat and jacket, I stealthily picked up my bags and tiptoed round the door. Slowly I edged towards the exit. Expecting any moment to hear cries of angry recognition, I stole down the steps, hoisted my wig-bag over my shoulder and sprinted away down the street as though the hounds of hell were after me.

'Don't upset yourself, dear girl, these things happen.' Freddy rose from his desk and gazed towards the library, through whose windows bright squares of light were already beginning to spread across the frozen lawn. 'You'll find, as you grow a little more experienced, that it becomes easier to take over the direction of a case and deal with things rather more decisively. Compromise where you have to but be prepared to stand firm. That's the way to earn respect in this profession.'

'Talking of that, Frederick, how about your postal wart-charmer?' queried David Jermaine from the wing-chair, stretching out a foot in the direction of the fire. 'Minced her up and left her for the dogs as anticipated, I assume?'

'Oh, we settled in the end,' Freddy said lightly. 'Did I hear Norman say that the Thornbarrow case was in the warned list, by the way?'

'Don't try to change the subject, Tobin,' persisted Jermaine. 'With all this talk of firmness and decision, tell us how you came to be making callow compromises with a lady you told us hadn't a leg to stand on?'

'There were ramifications; this and that . . .'

'Meaning?' Jermaine was enjoying himself.

'Well, it seemed arguable – just – that postal wart-charming might be a business within the meaning of the Act . . .'

'I believe you, dear boy, a hundred per cent,' Jermaine assured him. 'What was the lady like, incidentally?'

'I wouldn't attempt to deny that there was something . . . I'm not a fanciful man, but I must say there was something about that woman which gave me a distinctly creepy feeling. I found myself wondering, you know, assuming for a moment that if it were possible to charm warts away by post, it must also be possible . . . conversely . . .'

'To send them?' David Jermaine gave a shout of laughter. 'Tobin, that's the biggest piece of arrant nonsense I've ever heard in my life. And do you mean to say you've settled this case as a matter of pure cowardice, not to mention primitive superstition . . .'

'I mean to say nothing,' said Freddy Tobin with dignity, looking down at his immaculate shoes. 'Save, I am relieved to tell you, that at least I can still Vouch for my Feet . . .'

15

'Animals and the law don't go together, in my experience,' said Graham Webster. 'The moment you get livestock in a case it's nip and tuck how the thing will turn out.'

'With the emphasis on nip, if your experience is anything to go by,' said Jim Harbutt. 'Did Charlotte ever hear about that time when . . .?'

'Charlotte wouldn't be interested,' said Graham hastily.

'Changing the subject a moment. Was it you complaining about the chambers typist, Graham? Here's a good one . . .' Jim read from a crisp sheaf of papers:

'Further or in the alternative the defendant failed to take any or any adequate steps to prevent the said low-slung boob from swinging across the workbench so as to cause injury to the plaintiff.

'She'll just have to make a clean breast of it. Ho, ho. Sorry, what were we talking about?'

'Charlotte and I were discussing livestock,' Graham said. 'She's got a case on tomorrow involving animals.'

'Yes, I've come to pick your brains as usual. I thought you might be able to give me some tips.'

'I'll give you one here and now.' Jim's black eyes held a wicked gleam. 'Depending on the type of animal, of course, you want to be a bit careful in conference. As I was mentioning before, young Graham here got attacked by a client once, didn't you, Graham? What was it again? Something exotic, I remember. A wolf?'

'Somebody's pet mongoose,' said Graham.

'A mongoose wouldn't have been tall enough, surely?' remarked Jim.

'It stood on tiptoe, obviously.'

'Where did it bite you, then?' I inquired.

'In Croydon. More than that I do not propose to say. Comments were bandied about at the time which I considered to be in rather poor taste actually, and if you were about to come out with some ill-considered jape about baboons, Harbutt, I should advise you for your own sake to refrain.'

'It's being pecked I'll have to look out for,' I said. 'The case seems to be about hawfinches.'

'That sounds rather unusual,' Jim commented, hunting round his desk top. 'What have they been up to? Don't tell me, pavement nuisance? Defacing public monuments?'

Graham turned to me. 'Now, who's your client?'

'A man called Gilpitt. He's being privately prosecuted, this is at the magistrates' court, for having these birds . . . "recently taken in contravention of the Protection of Birds Act 1954", according to the summons.'

'Recently taken from what?'

'Well, from the wild, I think.'

'Oh, I see. The point being, I assume, that one is only allowed to keep birds bred in captivity and not go pinching them out of the woods or whatever . . . Jim, if you're looking for that writing implement, I can see it sticking out behind your ear.'

'Don't be ridiculous. Good lord, quite right, so it is.'

'Who's bringing the prosecution?'

'"The National Organization of Keepers of Native Ornamental Bird Species,"' I read, giving the portentous title full weight.

'Some bunch of crackpots, by the sound of it,' said Jim. 'What's this man's defence?'

'He says they were bred from birds which were originally sent to him in the post.'

'I shouldn't let him say that if I were you, Charlotte,' Jim said. 'Sounds one hundred per cent implausible to me, and even if it were true the bench wouldn't like it. People don't send each other birds in the post, or shouldn't. Might as well say they were baked in a pie.'

'I think what he means is, he had eggs sent by a breeder. Mr Gilpitt's an ornamental bird fancier, apparently.'

'I shouldn't be surprised if the ornamental Mr Gilpitt didn't turn out to be as crackpot as the National Bird Keepers Association or whatever it was.' Jim was following a train of thought. 'Bird-fanciers have a tendency that way in my experience. I had a relative once who used to keep birds. Looked like one himself as a matter of fact: little wizened fellow; beaky nose, beady eyes – altogether an odd fish. He came to a bad end, caught fowl pest or something, I forget.'

'Jim,' interrupted Graham. 'Is there to be some point to this story other than to illustrate your shocking disregard for the fate of some poor old relative of yours that neither Charlotte nor I has even met?'

'No "poor old relative" about it. In fact, to be perfectly honest,' said Jim candidly, 'I didn't like him a lot. Rather sinister, I thought, but then I'm not keen on people who keep things in cages.'

'No, nor am I,' I said. 'Or globes either, but I must say that from the short statement I have Mr Gilpitt sounds quite a decent person.'

'Hm' said Jim.

'Don't forget to take *Stone* with you in case you need to check any points of procedure,' said Graham more helpfully.

'Here, what's happened to my fountain pen, does anybody know?' asked Jim. 'It was here two minutes ago, now it's vanished.' On the point of beginning a fresh hunt across his desk top, he paused. 'You know, on reflection,' he said slowly, 'this has happened too often to be a coincidence. I'm not at all sure Fate isn't trying to tell us something. What time is it? Six o'clock . . . Yes, there you are; as I suspected, the hand of destiny is pointing us inexorably in the direction of El Vino's. Who are we, friends, to defy destiny?'

The next afternoon was jewel-clear and hot, one of those strange summer days which sometimes come from nowhere at the beginning of spring. Weighty with *Stone*, I approached the court through municipal gardens bright with martial rows of red and yellow tulips, taking in the scent of warm flowers and watching out for my instructing solicitors' articled clerk, Mr Dawlish. Or was it Devenish? I really must try to make more effort to remember names. It was lucky, I reflected, that I at least never forgot a face. Although I had only done one case for him, I could remember this Dawlish or Devenish perfectly well and would recognize him as soon as I saw him: fiftyish, grey-eyed, stocky and balding; wearing either a toupee or a green muffler, I could not quite recall which.

'Miss Hunter?' inquired a soft voice at my elbow and out of the courthouse porch stepped a willowy young man wearing a custard-coloured suit and a soft moustache with an impermanent look about it, as though a furry caterpillar had paused to rest on his upper lip. 'Glyn Devereux, of Partridge & Grebe.'

Of course, I remembered the name now. How was it that, although my memory for faces was perfectly good, names always slipped my mind? Feeling that I might have offended Mr Devereux by my blank expression, I tried to put matters right with an enthusiastic greeting.

'Certainly, certainly, yes indeed; how nice to see you again. What a pleasure,' I cried heartily, adding with imbecile zest: 'And a particular pleasure on such a splendid afternoon, I must say.'

'Hellehr.' Devereux extended a languid hand and looked at me as though suspicious that I might have been affected by the heat. 'Ah, Miss Hunter, meet, ah, Mr Gilpitt.'

I suppose that I had unconsciously expected someone resembling Jim Harbutt's unsavoury old relative, so I was greatly surprised to see, standing behind Mr Devereux and nodding amiably over his head like a sunflower, a great fair-haired giant. A huge hand enveloped mine as carefully as though it had been a fledgling chick. As Mr Gilpitt stepped out of the porch I was able to inspect him more closely: he was about thirty years old, with big blue eyes in a round, weather-brown face haloed by springy golden curls. It was an open face with a guileless kindliness about it and when he grinned, as now, it was as if a light had been lit inside a jack o'lantern. Anything less sinister would have been impossible to conceive. Indeed, it took such an effort of imagination to picture this vast sunny-looking individual slinking about in the underbrush netting wild birds that I began to feel the first prickings of professional intuition which gradually hardened into certainty that the prosecution had made a mistake.

I was introduced next to Mrs Gilpitt, a dark, thin girl with a brittle-boned appearance.

'Ah, Miss Hunter,' said Mr Devereux as something of an afterthought. 'This is our ornithological expert, Mr Flummereh.'

'Flannery,' said the expert in a gravelly voice which suggested northern origins. He was a small, shaggy-looking young man in socks and sandals and wearing, rather surprisingly in the heat, a fastened duffel coat with tartan hood. Wound round his neck was a crumpled cotton muffler with a loud Indian pattern on it. I found myself wondering about his qualifications.

'Er, Mr Devereux, I don't believe I've had a proof of evidence from Mr Flannery, have I?' I queried.

'That would, ah, be corrict, regrittableh. Mr Flummereh has only come into the picture, ah, more or less recentleh.'

From the way he spoke, it might have been thought that the expert had just been found under a bush ouside the court. By the look of Mr Flannery, it must have been a bramble bush.

So you expect me to take a statement from this man, do you? I thought wrathfully. I'm supposed to do your work for you while you sit like a barnacle on the wall there sunning yourself, you boneless, idle tapeworm, you creeping parasite.

I squeezed out a thin sycophantic smile. 'I quite understand, Mr Devereux,' I said. 'To save time, though, I wonder if you might be able to jot down a brief statement – just to give me some idea of Mr Flannery's evidence – while I have a word with Mr Gilpitt?'

'Nutrulleh, if that's what you wish,' said Mr Devereux, appearing exhausted at the thought of this wearing prospect. 'Well, come along, Mr Flummereh.' Rising, he seemed to pause in the hope of a reprieve: then, seeing there was to be none, trailed away into the courthouse followed by the short figure in the Indian scarf.

I took Mr Devereux's place on the low wall and motioned Mr Gilpitt to sit beside me. His wife, I noticed, had disappeared.

'Where's Mrs Gilpitt?'

'Nipped off home,' said my client in a soft, flat voice oddly at variance with his husky appearance. 'Yas.'

'I hope she'll be coming here to give her evidence?' I asked anxiously. Mrs Gilpitt was our only supporting witness on the facts and I hoped she would soon be nipping back.

'Oh yas, she won't be many minutes. Just gone to fetch up the corpses, actually,' he explained, adding, no doubt very sensibly, 'Wouldn't have done to have let them thaw out too soon. Could have got a bit nasty in this heat.'

'Oh. Yes, I see,' I lied, racking my brains to remember if there had been any mention of corpses in my brief. Surely I would have remembered? As it seemed unlikely that I could probe much further without revealing my ignorance, I decided that all I could do was to wait and see whose remains were being brought. It occurred to me that Mr Devereux would be glad that I could not ask him to take witness statements.

I opened my notebook and turned to a clean page. 'Well now, Mr Gilpitt, I've read your statement to your solicitors. Is there anything you wanted to add or are you happy about it?' My choice of words was unfortunate, as I at once realized.

'Happy?' said Mr Gilpitt slowly. 'You know, I've just about forgotten what it is to be happy. Birds are my life and this is the worst blow I've ever had. Yas, trimmed my pinions for me, this has.' He sighed and ran a hand sadly through his burnished curls. 'And even if they throw out the case against me, the National Organization can still refuse me a licence. How do you rate my chances?'

'A lot depends on whether the court accepts the inspector's evidence that there was no nest in the cage,' I replied cautiously. 'Had Mr Probus any reason at all to tell lies, do you think?'

This seemed quite unlikely and I was surprised when Mr Gilpitt nodded in a mysterious manner. 'I've come across Probus at bird shows,' he confided with a quick look round. 'And I believe he's jealous of my good wits.'

'Of your . . .?'

'I've a pair,' he said with pride. 'They got an honourable mention at the Bird Fair last year.'

'Oh, godwits . . .'

'And at this year's Fair I'm hoping they'll bring me a ribbon. Oh yas.' Mr Gilpitt's namby-pamby voice reminded me of the old song about bonny brown hair.

'Perhaps Mr Probus overlooked the nest?' I suggested. 'Would it have been hard to see?'

'Anything's hard to see out of the back of your head,' said Mr Gilpitt powerfully if not very helpfully. 'That Probus calls himself an inspector. Gor, he couldn't inspect his own backside. It's wicked, wicked . . .' Suddenly his anger seemed to die. Turning to me, he held out both his great hands like a suppliant. 'Do I look the sort who would harm a bird? Nobody's ever accused me of cruelty in my life before.'

'They're not accusing you of it now; just of catching wild birds and keeping them in cages. Although, I'm bound to say,' I added with unusual frankness, 'that a lot of people would consider it cruel to keep any bird shut up, however well it's looked after.'

'They can't have thought of the dangers a wild bird has to face,' my client said. 'Predators, injury, starvation, drought . . . People say birds oughtn't to be bred in cages at all, they ought to be let go free: fair enough, but isn't it better to be free from worry? Look at mine. Three hundred and sixteen specimens I've got in my cages at home and they get the best. They don't have to worry where the next meal's coming from; they have me to look to, like a dad.' I glanced at his face to see if this were intended as a joke, but saw only painful sincerity written there. 'It costs, mind you, but I could never have too many. I love every one of those little creatures as though they were my children. Well, by adoption . . .' he added, with a sad attempt at a joke. 'Tree pipits . . .' said Mr Gilpitt with rising emotion. 'Redstarts, warblers, hawfinches . . . all safe and sound.' Suddenly he hauled out a handkerchief the size of a pillowcase and blew his nose violently. I saw that the round blue eyes were damp.

At this stage our conference, such as it was, was interrupted by the reappearance of Mr Devereux with Mr Flannery in tow. It had been, Devereux informed me, unfortunately not possible to find a place to confer in private. They had wandered here and there, then realized after a while that time was getting on. Suspecting that I might be waiting to speak to the expert, he had brought him back with the least possible delay. On reflection, Devereux felt that it had been for the best, as I should now be free to exercise my discretion about the information I wanted from Mr Flummereh, wouldn't I?

'Eh up,' said Mr Gilpitt unexpectedly from the wall. 'Here comes Ethel with the corpses.'

Sure enough, little Mrs Gilpitt could be seen bobbing across the grass towards us carrying a very small polythene sandwich bag, which on arrival she handed to me, saying this was what I had been wanting. The bag was rather steamed up but peering inside I could just make out the barely feathered remains of four baby birds, none the less pathetic for being somewhat decomposed. Having thanked her gravely for this contribution, I handed the bag ceremoniously to Mr Devereux.

Unfortunately the sight of the small casualties had unsettled Mr Gilpitt and, seeing that he was in his pillowcase again, I asked Mr Flannery if he could spare a moment. We walked some way off and sat down on another part of the wall. The sun boiled down and I debated whether to take off my Bulgarian jacket but regretfully decided that it would be unprofessional. Mr Flannery, I noticed, still wore his duffel coat toggled up to the chin. Perhaps he was not warm-blooded?

'Now, Mr Flannery,' I began. 'Perhaps I can start by making a note of your academic qualifications?'

'I hold degrees from the universities of Nottingham and Keele,' said the expert in a tone which matched his bramble-bush appearance. I wondered if he was angry about anything in particular or generally disillusioned with Life, as I had heard many intellectuals were.

'Er, in what subjects, if I may ask?'

'Politics and economics,' said the ornithological expert.

A short time elapsed as I tried to think how to put the next question without sounding offensive.

'I was wondering . . . have you had much to do with, er, birds, Mr Flannery, in fact? – Or . . .'

'Or?'

'Or . . . not?'

'I am here today in my joint capacity as a friend of Mr Gilpitt and as a licensed member of the National Organization of Keepers of Native Ornamental Bird Species, if that was what you were wanting to know.'

There seemed little to be gained by saying that I had been wanting to know that he was an ornithological expert. At least we had in our favour the fact that, whatever his evidence turned out to be, this prickly young man would give it with such abrasive authority that it should be bound to carry weight.

'Well, Mr Flannery,' I said, hoping to save time by a bold global sweep. 'What can you tell me then?'

He stared at me with calm intellectual scorn. 'That rather depends what you ask, doesn't it?'

I looked coldly at this ornithological pig in a poke, trying to think of some remark which would pull the carpet from under his feet. As nothing came to mind, I said as acidly as I could, 'This is a serious business.'

'Serious? You call it serious? Yes, you can call it that if you like,' he conceded. 'Ah, but that's only a single dimension. Look at it on the Higher Body plane and what have you got?'

I had no idea but thought it sounded slightly occult.

'You've got a can of worms. A boiling can of worms.'

From time to time I have taken part in a conversation in which, try as I might, I can understand nothing the other person is saying. It does not happen often, but when it does the frustration and embarrassment are hard to describe. I began to wonder if by ill luck this was to be one of those conversations.

'The ironic thing of course,' went on Mr Flannery, 'is that it was old Gill's application lifted the lid off as regards the Higher Body. Thrown himself away with the boiling bathwater, as you'd say. And now since Knock-Knees come down on his head . . .' Flannery shook his own head morosely. 'As good as blown his bollocks off, if you ask me; in the bird world, that's to say, if you follow my drift.'

'Ah,' I said.

There was a silence. Then, as some further remark seemed to be expected, I seized on the only part of the speech I had followed. 'Who is Knock-Knees?'

'Not who, what. It's an abbreviation: NOKNES. It stands for National Organization of Keepers of Native Ornamental Bird Species,' said the expert. 'I would have thought you'd have known that if you'd read your brief.'

'Yes, but it doesn't stand for it,' I objected, stung by this piece of rudeness and feeling myself at last on sure ground. 'That would be NOKNOBS, surely?'

'Whoever heard of a serious organization called NOKNOBS?' Flannery gave a sarcastic crack of mirth. 'They called the National Economic Development Council NEDDY,' he added after a moment. 'Why? because if they'd called it NEDC nobody would have been able to pronounce it.'

Having delivered this clincher, Flannery nodded several times in a satisfied manner and undid his duffel coat.

I decided that a technical approach might be more successful. 'Tell me, Mr Flannery, is there some way in which an expert like yourself can tell the difference between a wild hawfinch and one bred in captivity?'

'Basically the plumage.'

'Could you perhaps enlarge on that?'

'Broadly, where there's a deficiency in a substance called carotene which occurs in natural habitats there can be a resulting loss of coloration.'

'Ah, I see. So birds bred in captivity are paler than those in the wild? That's what you're in effect saying, isn't it?'

'No.'

'Aren't they paler then?'

'It doesn't invariably follow. Some natural habitats are carotene-deficient.'

'So are you saying that birds from one particular habitat will tend to be paler than others?'

'No, I shouldn't say so.'

'Oh. Why not?'

'Because they don't tend to stay in one particular habitat. They migrate, interbreed and so on.'

'Could you say as a general rule that birds in captivity tend to be paler than in the wild?'

'Well, you could, but it would be wholly inaccurate. Breeders, you see, tend to feed their birds red pepper.'

'They do what? Feed them pepper? Why?'

'Red pepper contains carotene,' said the expert.

'Ah,' I said, seeing some light at last. 'So what you're actually saying is, I think, that birds in captivity . . .'

'Some birds in captivity . . .'

'Yes, thank you. Some birds in captivity which have been fed red pepper would tend to be darker than in the wild?'

'No. I wouldn't say darker.'

'Just not paler?'

'Right.'

'Mr Flannery, could you tell a captive bird from a carotene-deficient wild bird from looking at the plumage?'

'Possibly, if the breeder had been feeding pepper.'

'So, to summarize . . .' I said rather desperately.

'Aren't you forgetting something?' asked the expert.

'What d'you mean?'

'The hawfinch chicks had no plumage,' said Mr Flannery.

Having been promised that his train fare would be paid from Nottingham and back, Mr Flannery took his premature release from the case with surprisingly good grace and made off looking almost cheerful. Well, he had good reason, I thought, watching his grey back sink below the municipal horizon; the way this case was going I should have felt none the worse for going home myself. I heard a murmuring sound and turned to find Glyn Devereux at my elbow.

'. . . Dreadfully pushed at the office, ectualleh, so unless I can be of any further help I really feel I ought to desh away.'

'By all means, Mr Devereux. Goodbye and thank you for all your assistance,' I said with the smiling grit of a captain whose ship is sinking fast. 'I'll let you know how it goes.'

'Oh yes, rather. Right. Well, I'll just rush awf then.' He turned and began ambling slowly away through the flowers but had only gone a short distance when he turned back. 'My memoreh . . . I must be going senile.'

With a boyish trill of laughter, he drew from his pocket the polythene bag full of corpses and handed it to me ceremoniously like a talisman.

16

'Oh, I am a silly fellow, yes I am,' announced Mr Gilpitt with a masterly assessment of his own personality. 'I as good as forgot to give you this.'

He handed me a notebook on the front cover of which were the words STUDBOOK – HAWFINCH in woolly black letters.

'I've recorded it all down here,' said Mr Gilpitt, 'from the nesting up to the time when Knock-Knees jumped on me. Will it help? Mr Devereux thought it would.'

'That's excellent, Mr Gilpitt. Mr Devereux was quite right. In my view, a contemporaneous record like this showing the various events as they occurred should give a good deal of support to your evidence.'

It seemed a pity Mr Devereux had not thought of showing me this a little earlier to give me more time to study it.

'Never mind. All's well that ends well,' I said out loud, without thinking.

'Wish it hanged well had ended,' said Mr Gilpitt. 'This business has got me all of a dither. And there's something important I've forgotten to do.'

'What's that?'

'I've forgotten. Gor, I'll be glad when it's all over.'

Hoping he would have cause to be glad, I led my party into court.

It was like an old schoolroom filled with long wooden benches and tables defaced here and there by carved messages from days long past. The desk where I put my notebook bore the inscription B.O. WAS HERE – 1910. It was still here, I noticed: a rank musty smell which mingled strangely with the overall scent of warmed-over varnish and dust. Through leaded church-hall windows the sun torchbeamed down in little streams to make bright puddles on the parquet floor. The bench was high up, like the poop of an old tea-clipper, and from it glared down the fierce windbattered

features of an ancient mariner wearing naval blazer and long
side-whiskers, who, as we entered, was advising the court usher
to shake a leg in a quarterdeck bellow which blew that old lady
across the room like a paper dart. The strange seafaring expres-
sions which peppered his speech made this chairman a source of
puzzlement – the more so when I later found out that he was a
retired librarian who had never been to sea in his life. His fellow
magistrate was a hook-nosed woman in a green suit with a
matching hat from which a bunch of long green feathers curved
downwards, giving the unfortunate impression that she would
not have looked out of place perched on the chairman's shoulder.

'Sir, case number seventeen on your list: *NOKNES* against
Gilpitt,' said the magistrates' clerk. Mr Probus, the NOKNES inspector, got up to make his opening speech for the prosecution.
He was a smallish middle-aged man who appeared uncomfortably
warm in a dark pinstriped suit a little too tight for him. As befits
an inspector, he had a long tapering nose, and the little darting
eyes behind rimless glasses gave him a sharp inquisitorial air.

By using their sole witness for the prosecution to conduct their
case, NOKNES must have been trying to save legal costs. However
commendable this may have been in principle, it was soon seen
to have practical disadvantages, for Mr Probus – who seemed
equally inexperienced as an advocate and as a witness – kept
getting his dual roles entangled, provoking angry blasts from the
poop deck which flustered Mr Probus and made matters worse.
The confusion was intensified by Mr Probus the advocate's habit
of referring to Mr Probus the witness in the third person, perhaps
feeling that it gave his case more weight but in fact adding to the
cast-list in a baffling manner.

'The prosecutor then,' said Mr Probus the advocate, 'asked to be
shown to the aviaries. The inspector was able to note four specimens
of *motacilla lugubris*. Mr Probus then asked the defendant –'

'*Motacilla lugubris*? What's that? Some kind of bat, would it
be?' demanded the chairman.

'*Motacilla lugubris*, your worship, is the species commonly
known as the pied wagtail,' said Mr Probus a little smugly.

'I'm not having bats in this case,' stated the chairman firmly.
'Quite irrelevant. Splice up your mainbrace, Mr Probus. Come
here to deal with hawfinches and deal with them we will. Can't
keep yawing about here or we'll be running aground. Very well.'

'Mr Probus next,' said Mr Probus, chastised, 'inspected a pair of godwits. It was the inspector's belief that these birds have been taken —'

'Are you calling this inspector to give evidence?' interrupted the chairman.

'Well, yes, sir, that's to say . . .'

'Make up your mind, man, get your tackle in order. If you're going to call this inspector, whoever he is, I daresay he'll tell us himself what he believed, if it's admissible. We don't need to hear it from you.'

'Well, the inspector's myself, actually,' said Mr Probus.

'This is very far from clear, forgive me,' said the lady in green. 'I at one time believed you to have been Mr Probus. If you were the inspector, who was he?'

'I am and was also Mr Probus,' said Mr Probus, adding by way of clarification, 'That is, both in my private capacity and as an inspector.'

'If what you mean is that all these people were in fact yourself, why the deuce don't you say "I went" or "I requested" or whatever it is, instead of leading us to think there were any number of people involved in this confounded inspection of yours?' snapped the chairman. 'Waste of the court's time. We're not psychic, you know,' he continued irritably, as though poor Mr Probus had asked for a quick horoscope. 'Take a few reefs in this opening of yours, that's my advice, or we'll be hove to before we know where we are. Very well, let's get under way.'

Mr Probus carefully drew breath. 'Your worships, I then asked to be shown the hawfinch nest. There was none to be seen. At this time Mr Gilpitt made the following comment to me which I noted down in full. I quote . . .' he began significantly.

'Mr Probus,' barked the chairman, 'This isn't an opening speech at all; you're giving evidence, man. I very much trust you are not proposing to call yourself as a witness and go through the same matters again on oath?'

My opponent looked sheepish.

'Haul in your sheets, Mr Probus; the place for evidence is the witness-box, not here,' said the chairman crisply, as though the prosecutor had been caught out in some indiscretion. 'Oblige the court by taking the oath. Then you can sing out the facts and have done with it.'

The much tried Probus, who appeared far from singing, crossed the court and took the witness oath in such a hangdog manner that, had he not been unjustly prosecuting Mr Gilpitt, I could have felt sorry for him. Worse was to come for, as I soon saw, Mr Probus had written down his whole script on a piece of paper and was having difficulty in tailoring it to his sudden change from advocate to witness. The bench were for once sitting in expectant silence. Mr Probus stole a nervous upward glance, then lowered his eyes to his paper.

'Up anchor then,' said the chairman in a kindlier tone. 'Full speed ahead . . .'

Mr Probus licked his lips. Slowly he raised an arm and pointed across the court. 'This defendant, your worships, as the prosecution intend to prove,' he read, 'deliberately set out to ignore the law; to fly in the face of the Birds Protection Act 1954. He set his nets to capture fowls of the air, and catch them he did; in the woods, in the hedges, in the fields, in the byways, from hill to . . .'

'Mr Probus, this is a speech,' thundered the chairman. 'What we want is your evidence, not a lot of bombast. I am warning you, sir. This court has taken note of your various efforts to throw it off course by bringing in vampire bats one minute and non-existent inspectors the next, and our patience has been long but is now running out. Any more hanky-panky, Mr Probus, and I shall be obliged to call you to order.'

This threat caused the persecuted Probus to gulp in breath and charge through his evidence with such speed that even the chairman was left astern. I rose to cross-examine my weakened foe, knowing that now was the moment to fire that deadly torpedo of a question that would show Mr Probus up as a liar and demolish the prosecution case. Unfortunately just at present I could not think of one, but I hoped that as I went along something might come to mind.

'Well now, Mr Probus, when you carry out an inspection of a breeder's premises, what sort of things are you looking out for?'

Mr Probus's long nose appeared to quiver slightly. 'I am vigilant,' he said, 'for infringements.'

'Do you come across many infringements?'

The witness permitted himself a small rodent smile. 'My achievement record has been fairly high, yes.'

'Would it be true to say that you arrived at Mr Gilpitt's premises predisposed to find infringements?'

'I wouldn't say predisposed. I am vigilant but I hope I am also fair.'

'I'm sure we all join in that hope,' I said, with a meaningful upward glance at the poop deck. 'What was it about these fledglings which particularly aroused your suspicions?'

'There was no sign of a nest or a parent bird, and the fact that the fledglings were moribund suggested a lack of normal feeding procedures.'

'Are you saying you deduced the lack of a parent bird from the fact that the young were failing to thrive?'

'I didn't deduce the lack, madam, I witnessed it,' said Mr Probus. 'And failing to thrive isn't how I'd put it.'

'How would you put it?' I asked unwisely.

'Moribund, madam.'

'Ha, that's what you say, is it?' I said, thrown back on Harbutt rhetoric.

'It is,' said Mr Probus. 'And moreover, if I had had a camera, I would have taken a photograph of it.'

For some reason this statement seemed to carry almost as much weight as if he had actually produced a snapshot. I decided on a change of subject.

'I put it to you, Mr Probus, that there was in fact a nest.'

'No, there was not.'

'I suggest that it consisted of grass and sticks and a piece of Mr Gilpitt's old string vest?'

'All I can say is I saw no nest.' For a mad moment I wondered if he might be about to give evidence of the photograph he might have taken of the lack of a nest.

'Could you have overlooked it perhaps?'

'No. I was looking for it. I was vigilant.'

'I further suggest that the defendant told you he had put the female parent bird in another cage because she had a cough?'

'Madam, had any reputable bird-breeder made such a comment I assure you I would have made a note of it.'

'Sorry, my handwriting: he said she had got caught, presumably in the wires or something?'

'Nothing of the sort. If I may so put it, there was something about the whole matter which didn't . . . smell right, if you take my meaning.'

I took his meaning perfectly. I had for some time been noticing that the vague smell in the courtroom was becoming steadily worse. From the mustiness I had noticed at first it had ripened into a rich stench. When I sat down things were not quite so bad, but standing brought my nose into line with the nastiness, which seemed to be noticeable up on the bench too, for I had seen the woman in green stealing curious sidelong glances at the chairman. Now the chairman was beginning to look suspiciously in the direction of the clerk. For my own part I cut my cross-examination short and sat down, having failed to obtain Mr Probus's agreement that the whole of his evidence was a tissue of lies arising from a personal grudge about a pair of godwits, but earning a silent commendation from the bench for having kept up such a good head of steam.

Mr Probus stepped down from the witness-box and mentally shrugged himself back into his advocate's mantle. He shot a nervous look in the direction of the bench and I could sympathise with his feelings. NOKNES would have done far better to have briefed a barrister. It was unfair to expect an amateur to do something which was after all a matter of professional expertise.

'May it please you, sir, unless I can assist the court on any specific point at this stage, I do not propose to address you in opening.'

'No, thank you, Miss Hunter,' said the chairman, with every sign of being delighted at not to have to listen to a speech.

I called Mr Gilpitt. I was hoping while the bench were still feeling cheerful to get away with asking a number of irrelevant questions designed to show the depth of Mr Gilpitt's concern for bird welfare. This had impressed me; perhaps it might also make its mark on the magistrates, particularly if my client happened to burst into tears again.

'Tell us something about the various species of birds you keep,' I suggested, hoping this might trigger off Mr Gilpitt as before. Sure enough, he had no sooner begun to run through the list than emotion overcame him again.

'... Tree pipits and larks,' whispered Mr Gilpitt. 'Several kinds of thrush...' The round blue eyes brimmed with tears. 'I've wheatears, redshanks and a whitethroat,' said my client from his pillowcase: 'I've a pair of great tits —'

'Enough. That will do,' roared the chairman. 'Tell us, if you please, how many of these benighted creatures you hold in captivity altogether?'

'Oh, well over three hundred, your honour,' said Mr Gilpitt, who had clearly failed to gauge the mood of the tribunal. 'I only wish . . .'

'Er, yes, Mr Gilpitt, quite so,' I interposed, in case he might go on to say, as he had to me, that he wished it were double as many. Mr Gilpitt's views about saving birds from the wild, while sincerely held, were not necessarily very useful to our case.

'Over three hundred, you say? Creatures which might but for you have been in the wild? Did I hear you correctly, sir?'

'Yes, that's right, your honour,' said Mr Gilpitt, smiling through his tears. 'I look on all the specimens in my cages as my children,' said my client, blowing his nose.

'It's as well for you that the law doesn't, young man,' thundered the chairman. 'Or, believe me, you'd be facing extremely grave charges under the Children and Young Persons' Acts. Miss Hunter, the court will do its best to put aside the moral repugnance which it, and indeed any right-thinking person, must feel upon hearing this disgraceful catalogue – which, we bear in mind, is not the subject of the charge. We note in your client's favour that he appears, however late in the day, to be showing signs of remorse. I must warn you, though, to lose no time in setting a fresh course before you run any further aground than you have during the last few minutes.' He sniffed deeply before adding, 'There is something very unsavoury about this case.'

I could have hoped for a better start.

As my client went on with his evidence the noxious fumes became more poisonous than ever. The green lady leaned across and said something to the chairman, who shouted to the usher to open some more windows and look lively about it. I decided to play my trump card. From the way things were going it seemed unlikely that any of us would be looking lively for much longer. I handed up the hawfinch studbook.

'Mr Gilpitt, have you now prepared and do you now produce a contemporaneous record of the sequence of events relating to the breeding of these hawfinch chicks with which we are concerned?' I asked, with a grand disregard for the rule against leading questions.

'Oh yas,' said Mr Gilpitt, sounding a little vague but keen to please.

'With the court's permission, will you read out the first entry?'
Mr Gilpitt cleared his throat:

'*Day 1*: This morning Edith and I are thrilled to see the hawfinchs collecting nesting materials (goodbye to my old string vest!) in corner of cage. Now Edith and I look forward to a good lay!

'*Day 2*: Anticipation!

'*Day 3*: Nest complete. We are hoping for a good clutch soon (on floor of cage under plastic log).

'*Day 4*: . . .'

'Mr Gilpitt, haven't you logged down any dates?' said the chairman. 'This "Day 1, Day 2" business is all very well but we need to know the dates with some accuracy. When exactly did all this take place?'

My client scratched his head. 'To be truthful, your honour, you've got me a bit stumped there,' he conceded. 'Yas, you see, by the time I came to write it all down I couldn't rightly remember the dates as such . . .'

'When did you in fact make these notes?' chipped in the green woman.

'About an hour ago,' said Mr Gilpitt.

'This morning, d'you say?'

The chairman gave a kind of throttled roar and reared up in his chair in an ominous manner.

'Yas, sir. My solicitor happened to say it was a shame I hadn't kept a diary, as it would have helped; so I thought to jot it down would be no trouble to me, as well as being glad to help the court, naturally.'

'Help the court? I can scarcely credit what I hear.' The chairman's voice was like a cat o'nine tails. 'Contemporaneous, Miss Hunter, did you say? A journal of this kind, purporting to have been made at the time but in fact made yesterday or today or whatever it was, proves nothing and can serve no reputable purpose that I can think of.'

Nor I. I sat mortified, wondering how I could have forgotten to ask my client when those notes were made.

'Whether this was a deliberate attempt to deceive or whether it was designed as some kind of elaborate prank at the court's expense we have yet to discover.'

The chairman glared in outrage, first at my client's simple, good-natured countenance and then at my own before adding in a rather softened tone, 'Well, I trust that this can be put down to mental . . . er, inexperience on the part of you, Mr Gilpitt, or your legal adviser, as I warn you this court takes a dim view of any attempt to pull wool over its eyes, a very dim view indeed.'

Staring sightlessly at my notebook, I could imagine Mr Probus's face as though it were actually before me, rat teeth bared in a sympathetic leer. Still, I told myself there was a bright side. From now onwards things could only get better.

Although Mr Gilpitt managed to brush through the rest of his evidence without actual mishap, I was depressingly suspicious that we had lost the goodwill of the bench. When my client was testily advised for the second time to pile on canvas and narrow his bottom I decided that the time had come to sit down and leave him to Mr Probus.

Neither Mr Probus the advocate nor Mr Probus the witness had prepared us for Mr Probus the cross-examiner. Fixing a frosty glare on my client, he rose and slunk with a menacing face and bent knees towards the witness-box. Passing the clerk's table he snatched up the bag of corpses, took a sudden dramatic leap forward and waved it under poor Mr Gilpitt's nose. As he whirled it through the air, the source of the abominable smell became suddenly apparent. The hawfinch chicks had completely thawed out and were now showing themselves to be in a more advanced state of decomposition than could have been believed possible.

'Ha!' cried the prosecutor in a manner worthy of F. E. Smith, 'What have you to say about these, eh?'

Mr Gilpitt, struck dumb either by surprise or by the fumes, said nothing but gasped and recoiled.

'Well may you shrink in shame, Gilpitt,' said Mr Probus. 'It's my belief that these poor creatures were taken from the wild.'

'Take those things away, Probus,' Mr Gilpitt begged.

'Can't look them in the eye, can you, eh? I do not stop at that. It's my belief that not only your hawfinches came from the wild but also your godwits . . .'

I was on my feet in an instant. 'I object, sir. There has been absolutely no evidence –'

'Mr Probus, that suggestion was improper,' said the chairman. 'I shall order it to be struck forthwith from the court record.'

As the court clerk had been trying to beat away the fumes with his handkerchief at the time and nobody else appeared to have made a note either, the practical effect of this pronouncement was nil, but the chairman delivered it in such an impressive manner that I felt the point had been well made. On Mr Probus it had been entirely wasted. Like a horse which has scrambled over the last hurdle, he was bolting down the home stretch with a fanatical glint in his eye.

'You've been netting birds, Gilpitt; been doing it for years, haven't you? If you hadn't been netting the day I came, why did you pretend to have lost your nets, eh? Frightened to show them, were you, eh?'

'Nothing of the sort. That's slander, Probus.'

'I'll give you slander, you great booby,' said Mr Probus, forgetting himself. 'I suppose you've got your nets here to show the court?' he added sarcastically, Womble nose aquiver.

'As a matter of fact I have,' said my client. 'I thought you'd try to show me up but I'm not the fool you seem to think, not by a long way. Can I show them, miss?'

There seemed nothing else to be done but nod. I nodded.

'Look there,' said Mr Gilpitt.

He raised a hefty arm and pointed past the discomfited Probus towards the back of the court. A chance flood of sunlight blazed suddenly down upon the spectacle of little Mrs Gilpitt struggling to her feet burdened by armfuls of fine black mesh. As the light shimmered over the dark folds, it threw into bright and unmistakable relief something I would very much rather not have seen. The net was spangled like a starscape with a captive host of tiny telltale feathers.

'Gor. I remember now what it was I forgot to do,' said Mr Gilpitt.

I sat in the homebound train watching the last of the sunstreaked fields of young wheat recede before the red advancing army of brick and thinking back over the day. I was sad for Mr Gilpitt, whose one-man crusade to save birds from the hurly-burly of life in the wild had brought him such a poor reward: a hundred-pound fine, surrender of his nets, and presumably a lifetime of exclusion from the Higher Body.

The train wound its way into the station and stopped with a

heartrending sigh. Yes, it was sad for Mr Gilpitt. I picked up my briefcase and started to walk back along the platform towards the barrier. From one point of view the day had been lost, it was true. Yet I could not help but remind myself that from this day forward more and more small birds would be able to get up in the morning and go about their business unmolested – a prey to every sort of danger, it was true, but flying free. It was good to feel I had done someone a favour.

17

'Oh, Charlotte, there you are. I've got some good news for you.'

I looked up from the brief I was reading and saw Mo standing in the doorway of my room wearing a pleased expression. 'You know that awful drip you're trying to get rid of who follows you about?'

'Which one do you mean? Anyone who follows me about is a drip,' I said feelingly. 'Let's see, do you mean that terrible castoff of Billie's, Geoffrey, or the lecturer who kept wheezing Greek poetry down the collar of my blouse?'

'It was the gnome with the umbrella I meant, who stands about in the road.'

'Oh, Ashbagh.'

'That's it, Ashbag. I think I've got rid of him for you. I said you'd moved in with your boyfriend.'

'What boyfriend?'

'Oh, Charlotte, don't be so literal-minded,' said Mo in exasperation. 'Now all you have to do is lie low for a couple of days so he doesn't see you going in or out and you'll be rid of Ashbag for good.'

'But I've got to go out,' I objected. 'I've got my first jury trial down at Croydon tomorrow – at least it's supposed to be a trial, but I can't see it coming to a fight. If we've got a defence I haven't run across it yet . . .'

'Never mind about all that. Just make sure you get away early and back late until he loses heart,' said Mo. 'Of course, you could always move in with your wheezy lecturer, what's his name?'

'Didcot,' I said.

'Didcot? Good heavens, you can't be serious. Well, that settles it, he'll have to be got rid of as well,' said my energetic friend. 'He sounds even worse than Ashbag.'

'Nothing,' I said firmly, 'could be worse than Ashbagh.'

I had met Ashbagh one evening some weeks before when travelling home late on the underground. It was a blustery wet night and I had paused at the top of the steps to put up my umbrella when to my surprise a little wiry hand came stealthily up behind me from nowhere and grasped hold of the handle. I turned to look down into the face of a complete stranger. He must have been about twenty, I supposed, sallow-skinned with a beak of a nose and long sideboards which fluffed out into a straggly fringe beard. His hair, like himself, was dark, greasy and short. I did not like the look of him and my opinion was not improved when he gave me an ingratiating grin showing a great many snaggly whitish, and numerous blackish, teeth.

'Hello, hello, good evening. You will let me to walk together along your way?' He cocked a black eye at me in a half-wink. I glanced quickly around but the street was deserted. My heart sank.'

'I am Ashbagh,' said the youth, bumbling about inside the umbrella. How do you push the spocks up? No, I insist . . . Ah, there.' He held the umbrella gallantly erect. 'Now we can be comfortable.'

Comfortable was not the word I would have used to describe either my physical or my mental state. My feelings were an uneasy blend of sympathy, for a person so lacking in companionship as to have become expert at picking up girls, and embarrassment, apprehension and helpless annoyance at having been the one to be caught.

We plodded off together. It was still raining irritably in cold gusts. My physical discomfort centred on the fact that my companion was so short that the furthest stretch of his arm could not lift the umbrella above us both. The sodden cloth rested on the top of my head and I had the impression that if I stood upright I would sweep him off his little feet and carry him along clinging to the handle like a parachutist.

'Really, it's been very kind of you but I can manage.' I tried to take back the umbrella.

'Not at all. You must permit me. I am quite comfortable.'

Speak for yourself, I thought, sinking my head into my shoulders like a sea-turtle. I bent my knees almost double and shuffled along beside him feeling idiotic. From time to time my companion would shift his grip on the handle, tipping rainwater down the collar of my coat. Unwarranted though the situation was, I found I could not summon up the necessary force of character to be rid of him, though whether through fear of provoking him or of hurting his feelings I could not have said.

We had progressed, if progress it be called, for some thirty yards along the puddled pavement when he cleared his throat and said, 'Excuse me, do you come here often?'

'What, on the underground?'

'To the West End. To walk about in the streets at night. Do you often come?'

What did he think I was? 'I live here,' I said, instantly regretting it.

'Ah, then I shall have the pleasure of seeing you inside your home,' he said rather ambiguously. 'What is your name by the way? I am Ashbagh.'

'Sheila.' I said the first name that came into my head.

'Ah, Sealer. That is a pretty name. By the way, Sealer, when will you come out dancing with me?'

'I don't think I could, thanks very much,' I said politely, removing one of the umbrella spokes from my ear.

'You do not want to come out with me because I am black. I know, that is the reason, isn't it?' His voice was accusing.

'But you aren't black,' I pointed out, surprised into unusual frankness.

'Oh,' said Ashbagh. 'Well, if you do not consider me to be black, what reason could you have for not going out with me?'

This preposterous question robbed me of speech.

'Perhaps you are thinking I am too short for you,' he added. 'But this evening, you see, I am not wearing my boots.'

Luckily I was spared the necessity of an answer, for just then he missed his footing and disappeared over the edge of the kerb. He was standing disconsolately in the road still holding the umbrella in one hand and trying with the other to wring out one of his trouser legs when I seized the chance to say as kindly as I could, 'Well, goodnight. All the best,' and make good my escape. Since coming to the Bar I seemed to be doing a good deal of running, I thought, as I pounded along, hearing faint cries receding into the distance behind me. It was a shame about the umbrella but I was by now prepared to pay the price of freedom, however dear.

And that was the end of Ashbagh – at least so I thought, until one evening later in the week when Mo came in asking if anyone knew anything about a peculiar gnome-like man standing outside asking to be let into the building.

'He seems to be saying he thinks there's a seal in one of the flats,' she said. 'I couldn't make it out quite. I told him to get in touch with the zoo in Regent's Park but he's still out there. Another odd thing: he was standing under this pink umbrella with rosebuds on it, like yours, Charlotte, you know . . .'

I knew.

Since that time the pink umbrella had dogged me everywhere. I would look out of the window at odd times morning and evening and see it floating in the street below like a Portuguese man-o'-war. I was beginning to fancy that I saw it bobbing after me in crowds, even on trains and buses. Altogether, to hear Mo say that she had done away with my determined pursuer came as a great relief.

'I must say, Mo, it's been very kind of you.'

'Oh, it was nothing,' she said modestly. 'After all, what are friends for but to help each other, I say.'

I was about to respond when the telephone shrilled down the corridor.

'I'll get it. Perhaps it's Jo-jo,' said Mo, scrambling over the bed.

'If it should be Didcot for me, do you think you could tell him I'm out?' I begged.

'I'll do better than that. I'll tell him you've moved. Two birds with one stone.'

She was back a few minutes later looking depressed.

'Not Jo-jo?'

She shook her head. 'No, it was for you. I told him,' she said stoutly, 'that you'd moved out to live with your boyfriend in Brixton.'

'Oh, it was Didcot, then?' I asked eagerly.

'Well, actually, I was coming to that. Sorry I didn't twig until it was too late . . . I'm very much afraid it was your father.'

'Right now, Mr Duncan.' I had to shout to be heard above the din outside the Croydon Crown Court. 'I'll just run through the facts once again and you can tell me if I make a mistake. There were two officers. They came with a search warrant and between them they took from your back bedroom bottles of detergent, soap powders, brushes, polishes and so on, to the value of almost four thousand pounds. Four thousand: can that really be right?'

My client nodded. He was a spare-faced man with a shifty expression. 'So they said, aye,' he agreed. 'That's so.'

'But, Mr Duncan, at that rate your back bedroom must have been full to the brim, absolutely stuffed to bursting?'

'Aye, I suppose there was a fair bit.'

'May I just ask you: what did you intend to do with all these cleaning things?'

My client narrowed his eyes. 'Clean,' he said. 'The missus likes the place nice.'

'You weren't intending to, for example, sell anything?'

'Where could I do that?' asked Mr Duncan, all innocence. 'It might have been thought I'd pilfered the stuff.'

'Well, never mind about that,' I said, noticing that he seemed upset. 'What you say, at any rate, is that you've been employed as a cleaner for Supreme Cleaners Ltd for the past four years?'

'Aye.'

'And during that time you had permission from your employers to take any cleaning materials you wanted?'

My client nodded.

'Not just odd remnants, whatever was left in the bottle at the end of the week, for example? Could there have been a misunderstanding?'

'Old, new, whatever we wanted, whenever we wanted. I've had a mort more nor those police found over the time and no questions asked.'

'Yes, but "no questions asked" isn't quite the same as having permission, is it? How did your employers let you know you could take these things? Did they actually say, "Here you are, Mr Duncan, do take this brush or packet of dishcloths," or whatever it was? "Have this Brillo pad on us." Or how did it work?'

'They closed a blind eye to what went on,' said my client. 'No questions asked.'

'I'm afraid there are likely to be quite a lot of questions asked if you persist in fighting this case.' I shook my head. 'Did you tell the police about having permission to take the things? The police statements say nothing about it.'

'Aye, I tellt them what I've tellt yourself.'

'And what did they say?'

'They said I was under arrest for thieving.'

'I see.'

'Aye, the missus was disgusted. Flew at them and give them a piece of her mind.'

'What, for arresting you?'

'For taking the cleaning stuff. Wants it back, or compensation.'

'Well, we'll come to that in due course,' I said. 'In the meantime we have one or two problems. Have a look at this. D'you see, it's the statement of Mr Biffin, the managing director of Supreme Cleaners. He says, "Nobody had permission to take any item of cleaning equipment or materials off the company premises for their own use." Was he one of those who, er, closed a blind eye?'

'A blind eye, aye, aye . . .'

The ayes have it, I thought wildly. 'You know, I'm very sorry to say this, Mr Duncan, but I'm rather afraid a jury's going to have some trouble believing the account you've given.'

'It's the truth,' said my client. 'Or my name's not James Alfred Cadogan.'

'But your name isn't James Alfred Cadogan, is it? I mean, I have you down here as John Alfred Duncan. Has there been a mistake?'

For a moment my client's little blue eyes shifted uneasily this way and that. 'Nae, nae. Duncan, that'll do.'

'Yes, but . . . You're happy with Duncan, you're sure now?'

'Aye, aye.'

'Look, of course, naturally, I believe you a hundred per cent. But the jury, let me be quite frank . . . I don't think they're going to believe a word of it.'

'I'll take my chance.'

'They're going to call this Biffin as chief witness for the prosecution. He'll say what he said in his statement, that nobody had permission to take anything, and we'll be blown sky-high, take it from me.'

My client licked his lips and ran a palm over hair already plastered thinly to his skull like a cap. 'It'll be my word against Biffin, won't it?'

'Well, I suppose, basically, yes it will.'

'I'll take my chance then,' he said with every appearance of satisfaction. I found this confidence inexplicable until it occurred to me that Mr Duncan might not be aware how untrustworthy he looked. As I could scarcely point this out without giving offence, I racked my brains for a tactful way of preventing my unrealistic client from jumping into the jaws of disaster.

'There's also the matter of your record, Mr Duncan. With three previous over the years for theft from an employer, things could go badly if you were convicted. If you were to plead guilty and I were to explain in mitigation how you, well, fell victim to temptation seeing all those brushes and so on lying around or whatever, there's a chance of a fine or a suspended sentence. If you lead the court on a wild-goose chase and go down in the end, I don't need to tell you of the consequences.'

My client inspected me glumly as though I were a broken bridge. 'So you reckon I ought to plead guilty?'

'Frankly, yes I do.'

'Even though I didn't steal the stuff?'

'No, no, Mr Duncan, of course not. There's no question of my suggesting that you plead guilty if you, er, feel you didn't steal the goods. All I ask you to do is . . . think about it.'

'I've thought.'

'And you'd like to go ahead?'

'Aye.'

'Right then, we'll go in and put up the best fight we can.'

It crossed my mind that these, or something similar, might have been the last words of General Custer.

In the event we received a temporary reprieve, for as soon as he heard my client's plea of not guilty the judge – rather unexpectedly, as it was only half past twelve – decided to adjourn for lunch. My application for bail was refused and Mr Duncan was escorted down to have his meal as a guest of Her Majesty.

'He's finished a bit early, hasn't he?' I asked my opponent, a cheerful-looking young man a year or so senior to myself.

'Oh, old Shanks frequently does that: remands them in custody for a bit to give them a taste of what might be coming,' he remarked. 'You might well find when you next see your chap that he's decided on a change of plea.'

Sure enough, when I came back into court and saw my client in the dock, he was a changed man. True, he had not been exactly rubicund in the first place, but now he was so whey-faced and miserable that I felt sorry for him. A light dew of sweat gleamed on his upper lip and the little blue eyes held real fright. Her Majesty's hospitality had obviously left room for improvement.

'Listen,' he said hoarsely as I approached. 'Are you still advising me to plead guilty? Think that'll keep me out of there?' He indicated the staircase with a motion of the head.

'I don't know,' I said, 'but I still think there's a better chance if you plead than if you fight.'

'OK, I'll do it. Anything you say,' he said in a broken whisper.

'You want to change your plea? You're sure?'

I went back to my place, hoping my advice had been right. The terror of the man in the dock had reminded me that the only thing presently standing between Mr Duncan and prison was myself. I would not have been in his shoes for a great deal of money.

When the judge reappeared on the bench I got up and asked if the indictment could be put to my client again.

The judge looked pleased as the clerk briskly rose and read out the charge of theft once more. '. . . How say you, John Alfred Duncan, are you guilty or not guilty?'

My client cleared his throat. 'I've been told by my barrister to plead guilty,' he informed the court at large, 'but I didn't steal the stuff.'

In the silence which followed this announcement I ducked for cover, sinking my nose almost onto the desk and hunching up my shoulders against the stares of judge and jury.

'I can't see which one is my brief now. I know she's there somewhere.'

It seemed to me that every eye in the world was scanning counsel's row to see which barrister was trying to force an innocent client to plead guilty.

'Miss Hunter, what is this?'

I had to show myself then; merciful anonymity could not last. 'Er, well, your honour, there seems to have been a change of, er –'

'Very well, I shall record that as a plea of not guilty,' said the judge, forbearing to probe any further, for which I was extremely thankful. 'Let the jury be sworn.'

'. . . Finally, Mr Biffin, did any of your employees have permission to keep for their own use any cleaning materials or equipment belonging to your company?'

'Certainly not.'

I stood up to cross-examine with no very clear idea of what line of questioning would be the most effective. In fact I could think of nothing to ask this witness which would be of any effect except to underline the strength of the prosecution case. All I could do was to put my client's case to the witness and sit down again as quickly as I could.

'Mr Biffin,' I said with all the confidence of a person about to walk the plank. 'Er, you say no employee had express permission to take cleaning materials . . .'

'That's correct.' The witness, a large beefy man, gave me the sort of look a bull might give a bluebottle.

'But there is such a thing as implied permission, is there not?'

'How d'you mean?'

'Isn't it a fact that employees took materials?'

'Oh yes, that's true enough.'

'With the knowledge of the company?' I took another step out onto the springboard.

'Yes, that's correct.'

'Er, would it be fair,' I asked with growing incredulity, 'to say that the employers . . . turned a blind eye to the situation?'

'Yes, I think that would be fair.'

'Would it be fairly usual,' I persisted, aware that the question was incredible, 'for your employees to have substantial amounts of cleaning materials and equipment at home for their own use?'

'I should think so, yes,' said Mr Biffin.

'Mr Johnson,' said the judge. 'Isn't that the end of the prosecution case?'

My first jury trial was over in seventeen minutes. The jury, as they brought in by direction their verdict of not guilty, appeared as dumbfounded as I felt myself. Mr Duncan even got his compensation order. His missus would be able to keep the place nice well into the twenty-first century. I found it baffling. My client, however, as he quietly gathered up his things and waited to be let out of the dock, showed no surprise. He glanced up as I passed. 'There you are,' he said. 'You wouldn't have it but I told you I didn't steal the stuff.'

I made my way out of the court building into the spring sunshine still pondering on the extraordinary turn the case had taken and arguing with myself about my own part in it: had I been over-hasty in trying to persuade my client to plead guilty? Shouldn't I have been more ready to accept his version of events which, although it sounded incredible, had been shown to be the truth? After all, as Jim had rightly said, I was not the jury. Yes, my judgement had been at fault. From now onwards I would try to be more open-minded. I was ashamed of myself.

At the corner I paused and was about to cross the road when I happened to notice two men in deep discussion half hidden behind a hoarding. There was a conspiratorial air about them which drew my attention. Where had I seen them before, those heads bent together, one with the curly poll of a bull, the other with hair plastered thinly like a cap? . . . Mr Biffin and my client? What were they doing huddled there? There were certainly questions to be asked. Not by me, though. I was closing a blind eye. A little less ashamed of my judgement now, I headed for chambers.

'How did your trial go, Charlotte?' Graham asked as I puffed through the inner door into chambers' hallway. 'You won? Jolly good. How long were the jury out? You got off at half-time? That's a great success. Congratulations. Here, Norman,' he followed me into the clerks' room, 'do you hear what happened? Miss Hunter got the fellow off at half-time. Remarkable on those facts, I should have thought.'

'Well, it wasn't quite like that –' I began.

'Well done, Miss Hunter. Got him off on a submission, did you?' said Norman.

'It wasn't quite on a submission; it was before half-time, but . . .'

'Good heavens, even better,' Graham exclaimed. 'Good old Charlotte.'

'What's good old Charlotte done?' asked Jim, appearing from nowhere. 'Got the fellow off before half-time. How did you do it?'

'The first prosecution witness sort of fell to bits in cross-examination, but the thing was . . .'

'And the judge threw it out?' said Jim. 'Not bad. David, did you hear about Charlotte here? Broke down the chief prosecution witness in cross-examination. Judge slung it out.'

'Broken your duck, young woman? This calls for a celebration. Fred, come in here a moment. Haven't you got a bottle or two of Pommeroy knocking about for just such an occasion?'

'What sort of occasion?' said my pupilmaster, strolling in.

I listened as it was explained how by a stroke of inspired cross-examination I had demolished the prosecution, gained the congratulations of the bench and left the court with the glad cries of my astonished client and his family ringing to the rafters. I felt a twinge of conscience. Now, surely, was the moment to announce what an undistinguished part I had really played and set the record straight?

'Well, young Hunter,' said Freddy. 'A performance worthy of a pupil of mine. What higher praise can I bestow? Percival, dig out that half-dozen I got in this morning. We shall drink to young Charlotte's first forensic triumph. May it be the first of many.'

I decided that the moment for confession was past. I would just hope that the real story never got back to chambers.

'Well, Miss Hunter,' said the walrus, 'the best of luck.'

I raised my glass. Within its glowing sphere, Norman, Percival, Graham, Jim and Mike, David Jermaine and Freddy Tobin seemed to float towards me on a rosy sea of good-fellowship. I thought what good luck I had already had.

And, as for me, had I accomplished anything? Had I changed at all from the girl who had arrived in chambers on that green morning nine months ago? Yes, I had gained much in experience. Forged like a horseshoe on the anvil of the law, I now knew with confidence that my days of looking a fool in court were over. It was a good feeling.

'What have you got on tomorrow, young Charlotte?' asked David Jermaine. 'First time in the companies' court? One word of advice: be brief. Old Razor Bill's a cranky bastard . . . Ask him to make the usual order. Don't worry. He'll know what you mean.'

Edward Vernon
Practice Makes Perfect 85p

Out in the waiting room lurk a confused old lady, a timid vet, a puzzled diabetic, a lonely housewife, a hypochondriac athlete, a tipster with an ulcer, a nun with dandruff, and a persistent young lady with abundant charms and perfect health!

Inside the surgery there is the general practitioner, filling out countless forms, outwitting the pill-freaks, destroying indestructible plastic syringes, watching pharmaceutical salesmen fill his office with gimmickry, and dreading the small hours phone call from a patient with a hangover!

'An entertaining and often hilarious look behind the surgery door . . . make a bedside book of it' DAILY TELEGRAPH

John Holgate
Make a Cow Laugh £1.75

To give up commuter life for the daily grind of a Welsh border farm takes something special. You might need imagination, dedication or just sheer lunacy . . . but you do need a sense of humour!

'Packed with humorous incidents . . . if his farming is as good as his writing he should have left London years ago' WESTERN MAIL

James Herriot
It Shouldn't Happen to a Vet £1.95

'Imagine a *Dr Finlay's Casebook* scripted by Richard Gordon and Thurlow Craig and starring Ronnie Corbett and you will understand why James Herriot is on to a winner . . . a delightful new collection of stories' SUNDAY EXPRESS

'His easy and at times excruciatingly funny case history narratives must rate as country classics and he throws in a stumbling, awkward courtship for good measure' FARMERS WEEKLY

Let Sleeping Vets Lie £1.95

The hilarious revelations of James Herriot, the now famous vet in the Yorkshire Dales, continue his happy story of everyday tribulations with unwilling animal patients and their richly diverse owners.

'He can tell a good story against himself, and his pleasure in the beauty of the countryside in which he works is infectious'
DAILY TELEGRAPH

Alan Burgess
The Small Woman £1.95

The amazing true story of Gladys Aylward, the parlourmaid who became a missionary in China where, with great faith and indomitable courage, she worked for twenty years.

When the Japanese came to bomb, ravage and kill, she led a hundred homeless children on a terrible twelve-day march over the mountains to the Yellow River and safety. Translated into many languages and filmed under the title of *The Inn of the Sixth Happiness*, the book is the inspiring record of the struggles and achievements of a most remarkable woman.

George Clare
Last Waltz in Vienna £2.95
the destruction of a family 1842–1942

On Saturday 26 February 1938 17-year-old George Klaar took his girl Lisl to his first ball at the Konzerthaus. His family were proudly Austrian. They were also Jewish. Just two weeks later came the *Anschluss*. A family had been condemned to death by holocaust.

'They are like actors in a Lehar operetta suddenly cast in the roles of a Greek tragedy' ARTHUR KOESTLER, SUNDAY TIMES

'Mr Clare leads us gently, but inexorably, to the edge of the pit and then leaves us to look down into it'
EDWARD CRANKSHAW, OBSERVER

Peter Tinniswood
The Brigadier's Tour £1.95

The Brigadier, his eye well and truly in, his opinions as inelastic as ever, his prejudices apparent, takes us on a gentle stroll through cricket's hall of fame, recalling great deeds both on and off the field of play, offering witty and perceptive, if sometimes confused and inaccurate, insights into the players who have pleased, charmed, amused and warmed him through his long relationship with the 'summer game'.

The Brigadier Down Under £1.75

In the not inconsequential tradition of *Tales from a Long Room* and *More Tales from a Long Room*.

'Esteemed reader, far, far the mountain peak, as one of our English poets essayed, yet not as far as the distant landscapes of Australia from the familiar surroundings of my own beloved Witney Scrotum . . . I could not but follow our own fine team to their Herculean test of leather and willow on the far-flung turf . . . Australia is a land disturbingly full of Australians . . . Not a place to which I took an instant affection. The lady wife was more adaptable, especially in terms of her powers of rainmaking and skill in the nets . . . I am not a prejudiced man, but . . .'

Gyles Brandreth
The Law is an Ass £1.75

Gyles Brandreth has gathered together a multitude of true tales from his legal acquaintances about the merrier side of justice. Ridiculous laws and ridiculous lawyers, pedestrian prosecutors and prosecuted pedestrians. A treasury of tales from the boozers round the Bailey and the caff behind the local nick. Here is the full panoply of justice in the act of splitting its sides.

Fritz Spiegl
Keep Taking the Tabloids £1.75

Exclusive - Spiegl On the Street! Meaning a survey by Fritz Spiegl of the contribution to contemporary popular culture made by the denizens of Fleet Street. *Keep Taking the Tabloids* shows the World According to the Hacks. A place where everyone not *hitting out* is *appealing*, where price increases are *slapped on* to make *costs soar*, where every ambulance is making a *mercy dash* and every inflamed chip pan is a *fire drama*. *Vice probe horror shock – bishop named* is an effective way to sell papers. So that's the way the industry is run. Now in these *exclusive and revealing* pages Spiegl shows you how it's done . . .

George MacDonald Fraser
McAuslan in the Rough £1.50

That walking disaster Private McAuslan, the dirtiest soldier in the world, is back for more misadventures – from the bars of North Africa to the fast greens of Scotland.

'A delight with a chuckle on every page' DAILY MIRROR

'An old sweats' reunion, the nearest we could hope to get to a neo-Kipling touch' GUARDIAN

The Pyrates £2.50

What have we here? Out yonder on the high seas of adventure are Pyrates! Can our impossibly handsome hero redeem the treasure and rescue his lovely lady from the lascivious clutches of Akbar the Damned? Read on, and all shall be revealed.

'It's all there, right down to a dead man's chest, cleavages that are everything they should be and characters in seaboots who say nothing but "Arr" or "Me, hearty!"' THE FINANCIAL TIMES

Fiction

☐	**The Chains of Fate**	Pamela Belle	£2.95p
☐	**Options**	Freda Bright	£1.50p
☐	**The Thirty-nine Steps**	John Buchan	£1.50p
☐	**Secret of Blackoaks**	Ashley Carter	£1.50p
☐	**Lovers and Gamblers**	Jackie Collins	£2.50p
☐	**My Cousin Rachel**	Daphne du Maurier	£2.50p
☐	**Flashman and the Redskins**	George Macdonald Fraser	£1.95p
☐	**The Moneychangers**	Arthur Hailey	£2.95p
☐	**Secrets**	Unity Hall	£2.50p
☐	**The Eagle Has Landed**	Jack Higgins	£1.95p
☐	**Sins of the Fathers**	Susan Howatch	£3.50p
☐	**Smiley's People**	John le Carré	£2.50p
☐	**To Kill a Mockingbird**	Harper Lee	£1.95p
☐	**Ghosts**	Ed McBain	£1.75p
☐	**The Silent People**	Walter Macken	£2.50p
☐	**Gone with the Wind**	Margaret Mitchell	£3.95p
☐	**Wilt**	Tom Sharpe	£1.95p
☐	**Rage of Angels**	Sidney Sheldon	£2.50p
☐	**The Unborn**	David Shobin	£1.50p
☐	**A Town Like Alice**	Nevile Shute	£2.50p
☐	**Gorky Park**	Martin Cruz Smith	£2.50p
☐	**A Falcon Flies**	Wilbur Smith	£2.50p
☐	**The Grapes of Wrath**	John Steinbeck	£2.50p
☐	**The Deep Well at Noon**	Jessica Stirling	£2.95p
☐	**The Ironmaster**	Jean Stubbs	£1.75p
☐	**The Music Makers**	E. V. Thompson	£2.50p

Non-fiction

☐	**The First Christian**	Karen Armstrong	£2.50p
☐	**Pregnancy**	Gordon Bourne	£3.95p
☐	**The Law is an Ass**	Gyles Brandreth	£1.75p
☐	**The 35mm Photographer's Handbook**	Julian Calder and John Garrett	£6.50p
☐	**London at its Best**	Hunter Davies	£2.90p
☐	**Back from the Brink**	Michael Edwardes	£2.95p

☐	**Travellers' Britain**	} Arthur Eperon	£2.95p
☐	**Travellers' Italy**		£2.95p
☐	**The Complete Calorie Counter**	Eileen Fowler	90p
☐	**The Diary of Anne Frank**	Anne Frank	£1.75p
☐	**And the Walls Came Tumbling Down**	Jack Fishman	£1.95p
☐	**Linda Goodman's Sun Signs**	Linda Goodman	£2.95p
☐	**The Last Place on Earth**	Roland Huntford	£3.95p
☐	**Victoria RI**	Elizabeth Longford	£4.95p
☐	**Book of Worries**	Robert Morley	£1.50p
☐	**Airport International**	Brian Moynahan	£1.95p
☐	**Pan Book of Card Games**	Hubert Phillips	£1.95p
☐	**Keep Taking the Tabloids**	Fritz Spiegl	£1.75p
☐	**An Unfinished History of the World**	Hugh Thomas	£3.95p
☐	**The Baby and Child Book**	Penny and Andrew Stanway	£4.95p
☐	**The Third Wave**	Alvin Toffler	£2.95p
☐	**Pauper's Paris**	Miles Turner	£2.50p
☐	**The Psychic Detectives**	Colin Wilson	£2.50p

All these books are available at your local bookshop or newsagent, or can be ordered direct from the publisher. Indicate the number of copies required and fill in the form below   12

....

Name_____
(Block letters please)

Address_____

_____

Send to CS Department, Pan Books Ltd, PO Box 40, Basingstoke, Hants
Please enclose remittance to the value of the cover price plus:
35p for the first book plus 15p per copy for each additional book ordered
to a maximum charge of £1.25 to cover postage and packing
Applicable only in the UK

While every effort is made to keep prices low, it is sometimes
necessary to increase prices at short notice. Pan Books reserve
the right to show on covers and charge new retail prices which
may differ from those advertised in the text or elsewhere